FIRST SCIENTIST OF ALASKA

William Healey Dall

FIRST SCIENTIST OF ALASKA

William Healey Dall

Born   Died
August 21, 1845—March 27, 1927

by EDWARD A. HERRON
author of DIMOND OF ALASKA

/\/\/\/\/\/\/\/\/\/\/\/\/\/\

JULIAN MESSNER, INC · NEW YORK

Published by Julian Messner, Inc.
8 West 40 Street, New York 18

Published simultaneously in Canada
by The Copp Clark Publishing Co. Limited

Printed in the United States of America
Library of Congress Catalog Card No. 58-10927

M.J.

TO CLARA

FIRST SCIENTIST OF ALASKA
William Healey Dall

CHAPTER ONE

"Douse that light!"

"Want them Confederates to blow us right off the streets of Boston? Get that light out, and get under cover, boy! They're coming in by sea!"

William Healey Dall slid off the high stool before the bookkeeping ledgers. He blew out the kerosene lamp and stood uncertainly in the darkness. Then he took a cautious step forward and fell over a footstool.

"Glory," he muttered, while he rubbed his shins, "what's all the excitement? How can any Confederate soldiers get up here in Boston? We're a thousand miles from Gettysburg!"

He scratched his forehead, trying to figure a possible route for the enemy, up the Susquehanna Valley of Pennsylvania, over a corner of New York State to Albany, then clear across the state of Massachusetts. "But that fellow said they were coming by sea!" He sauntered to the open doorway and looked over the sleeping city of Boston. "They can't be right."

Yet he could hear the thud of running feet on the thick wooden planking of India Wharf. In the distance, lost in the narrow, twisting streets, a voice lifted in a commanding shout.

The sound seemed to take life and spiral upward over the

[9

steeples and tin roofs of the city of Boston. It traveled like a thin cloud over the darkened water front. It drifted through the forest of spars high over the sailing ships that waited patiently on that night of July 3, 1863.

It was hard to keep his mind on the excitement that trembled over the city. He turned instead to the east, to the calm waters of Boston Harbor, and beyond that, past the barricading islands, Massachusetts Bay, and the broad sweep of the Atlantic Ocean.

The sea was a great home, he thought dreamily. How often he had tramped the beaches between Boston and Cape Ann in the early sunrise hours when the tide was low. There were rocks, and pools, and caves that he had marked as his very own, a world apart from this other world at war.

There were times, when he stretched flat upon a rock, peering into a pool of clearest sea water, that he felt guilty. For men were dying in war; brothers were fighting brothers. While he was engrossed in bright fish that darted in clear pools, in starfish of brilliant hue, in beautiful colonies of lacelike polyzoanes, strange tunicates, the living flowers of the sea, anemones, and the little crabs with their glossy shells, the world was bursting with excitement.

He had tried to become engrossed in the war, William told himself; he had spent all those nights on guard duty with the volunteers who tramped about the Boston arsenal. But his heart was never in it. His heart went to the sea, to the mud and the sand of the bays that were pierced with innumerable burrows, and out to the abyss of the ocean where huge whales lorded over fish and crabs and lobsters, starfish and sea urchins.

He looked at the gun in his hand as he tramped the lonely sentry marches, and shook his head. He wanted to be down by the beach, searching for clams and oysters on the bottom, alert for the sea snails with their curious shells, watching for mussels and barnacles that could tell a story with every twist and curve of their shells.

Because of his love for science, he felt detached from the other clerks in the office of Deshon and Yarrington, African traders.

One day Mr. Yarrington stood behind William's desk, a thin crumpled letter in his hand. "Seven weeks!" he exploded, "seven weeks and not a word about the *Eastern Trader*! Why, she could be at the bottom of the sea, and we'd never know! I'm telling you, young Dall," he said, "I hope with all my heart that second cable they're trying to lay across the Atlantic is a success! Then we'd know about our ships the very day they cleared the European ports headed for home! No more guesswork, no more worry, no more thinking they've been lost at sea."

William looked at him blankly. He was afraid he would be taken for a stupid blockhead. The cable across the Atlantic? Hadn't the first cable failed seven years before? Why, just the past week his mother had said the Atlantic would never be conquered by a submarine cable.

He was still trying to grope for an answer to Mr. Yarrington when Billy Sparks, the other junior clerk, spoke up brightly: "Western Union's going ahead great guns with its land telegraph that'll tie us into Europe, sir. They're halfway across Siberia and starting up through British Columbia to make the link-up somewhere in Russian America."

William looked at Billy Sparks enviously. If only he were alert to the things that were happening in the world all about!

Mr. Yarrington wasn't impressed. "Russian America!" he snorted. "They'll never be able to put a telegraph line through that wilderness. Eskimos'll steal the wire fast as they string it. What do you think, Dall?"

But William, his chin cupped on his clenched fists, was dreaming. Russian America (one day to be known as Alaska). Virgin wilderness. Ten thousand secrets waiting for the first scientist to go north.

"Dall! Do you hear me speaking to you?"

"Yes, sir, yes, sir? What is it, sir?"

"Oh, pshaw, boy, get back to your work."

And William turned back to his work, sadly. It was true. He was a dreamer. He loved his country, but all his intense sympathy was for the humble creatures of the sea.

This night of excitement, though, was different.

He was pulled back from his dreaming by a hoarse shout: "My foot! My foot! You've run over my foot with that dab-blasted thing! I got a mind to. . . ."

Down India Street a mob of men hauled and shoved at an ungainly object. They pushed and shouted, and screams and threats rose continuously in the air.

The mob came closer, grunting with its efforts to roll the big object over the uneven cobblestones of the street. Standing in the darkened doorway of the Deshon and Yarrington office, William watched in wonder.

The country was at war, North against the South. But until this fateful night the war had only been spelled out in news-paper headlines, or in wild, enthusiastic parades as the Mas-sachusetts Volunteers marched off to battle in distant states to the South.

"Golly," William whispered to himself, "maybe it's true. Maybe Lee did break through at Gettysburg. Maybe Boston is being invaded!"

"Hey, you! You in the doorway. Lend a hand here! We

12]

got to get this cannon mounted out on the wharf. Tonso McCrae and his *Shannon* are bringing in the Johnny Rebs by the sea! Five shiploads of them sneaking into Boston Harbor! Come on, give us a hand!"

William ran into the street. He placed his shoulder to the monstrous carriage on which the ungainly cannon was poised. Next to him was a little old man, his face almost hidden in a forest of whiskers. "Your daddy helping, son? That him up front?" he asked.

"My father's a missionary in India," William replied. His father? He had been gone eight years. Almost a memory.

"Well, don't matter. Just mind your feet, son. Don't let 'em get caught under the carriage. We sure ruined more toes on this trip down than them Rebs ever will, so help me."

"Is it true?" William asked while he strained with all his might on the gun carriage. "Are the Confederates really invading Boston?"

"True? Why, son, ain't you seen the fires burning out on Governors Island? Wouldn't surprise me if half of General Lee's Army is out there this very minute, ready to come in and cut the throat of every man, woman, and child in Boston!"

"But General Lee—how could he get here? He was down in Pennsylvania just yesterday, fighting at Gettysburg. How could he . . . ?"

"Boy, don't ask foolish questions. You just lay those big shoulders on this gun carriage and push! Hey, boy! Hey, you! Come back here!"

But William paid no attention. He straightened slowly and walked to the water's edge. Immediately above his head was the carved figure of a woman, the ornate bowsprit of a schooner newly arrived from Africa.

There was an odd smell about the small ship. Slavery had

[13

been abolished in Massachusetts for more than eighty years. Yet there were rumors of slave traders still busy even in the midst of the life and death struggle between the North and the South.

William looked beyond the bobbing stern of the schooner, out into the dim darkness that shrouded Boston Bay. "No fires on Governors Island," he said to himself, looking hard to the east. "Not a speck of light out there. Somebody's dreaming."

He looked down at his feet. Even in the darkness he detected a faint, silvery trail, the delicate night markings of a land snail. As though drawn by a magnet, William dropped to his knees, eagerly following the silvery line.

Suddenly the invasion was forgotten.

He followed the trail patiently. He lifted aside broken stones, pieces of burlap, a twig from an elm tree. He followed the silver shine over the thick wooden coping that lined the edge of Atlantic Avenue, ten feet above the lapping waters of the Bay.

Finally he came to his quarry. Secure in the night, the tiny snail munched contentedly on a piece of wilted lettuce that had drifted down the gutters from the public markets beyond Central Wharf.

William nodded his head in satisfaction. He struck a match and peered at the little horselike snail that rested contentedly beneath its spiraling shell. "Probably *Helix pomatia*!" William muttered. "Wow!" The match burned his fingers, and he flipped it hastily into the water. "But, then," he continued thoughtfully, "those markings . . . maybe I better send it down to the Smithsonian Institution in Washington, that is, if the Rebels haven't captured it yet. Let me check."

He put his hand into his hip pocket and brought out a well-worn book. Stretched flat on the wide timber coping, as though he were on the hearth before the fire at home, he thumbed the book. He turned the pages as if he knew every line and drawing by heart. Finally, he stopped, squinted at the page, and absent-mindedly struck another match.

The big yellow, spluttering flame leaped into the air, gasping a wide glow. By its light William read the fine print.

He looked from the illustration to the lettuce eater, then back to the book again. "This light," he muttered. "Can't be sure. Could be a kind never seen in Massachusetts before." He looked up at the bowsprit of the schooner hanging over him. "Might have been carried in from Africa on the *Helen*."

The match spluttered and went out. He tossed it quickly into the oily waters. It hissed and died away.

"Golly," William thought, as he watched the faint outline of the burned match bobbing in the current, "if a fellow could only get to some place like Russian America, and collect specimens." He shook his head regretfully. "Guess I'm lucky to have a chance to find out what's alive around Boston. Where is that little fellow?"

He struck another match and peeped into the crevices for the lettuce-surfeited snail. "Now where'd he get to in such a short time?"

"Get that man! He's giving signals to Johnny Reb! Grab him! He's a spy!"

Three men came racing out of the darkness of India Wharf. They threw themselves on William. One pressed a mighty arm around the boy's neck. Still another dove for his feet. The third threw his arms around the boy's waist, and all three started pulling in opposite directions.

CHAPTER TWO

Choking and gasping, William tried to cry out, but a hairy arm was thrust hard against his mouth. He listened in wonder to the shouts of the excited men.

"Come on, you spy! We caught you dead to rights! Giving signals to them Confederate ships out in the harbor!"

"Trying to get us all blown to glory!"

"We'll fix you! We'll show you how we treat spies up here in Boston!"

"Get a rope!"

William twisted his head around and gulped in a mouthful of the air. "I'm no spy!" he yelled.

"Don't you talk none, mister. We're doing the talking now. You had your chance with them signals."

"Grab that book! Quick! The spy's trying to throw it overboard!"

"I'm not trying to throw it overboard," William protested. "I wanted to put it back in my pocket so it wouldn't get lost."

"A likely story, my little Confederate spy! Code book, that's what it is!"

"It is not," William yelled, trying to free his head from the huge arm embracing it. "It's a book on mollusks!"

"Just what I thought," the man snapped. "A code book.

16]

We got us a spy all right. A real, honest-to-goodness, Johnny Reb spy."

"Listen," William said patiently, "if you'll only let me go, I can explain. . . ."

"You're not going no place, mister spy."

"But the book," William continued doggedly, "it's about slugs, and snails, clams, oysters, whelks, limpets, cuttlefish—oh," he said, fighting to his feet, "you wouldn't know if I drew pictures!"

"No, mister smart pants, all we know is a spy when we catch one."

"Shall we hang him now, or let the Major talk to him?"

"Down at Bull Run we didn't wait to see no officers. We hung the spies first, then brought the bodies to headquarters."

"You can't hang me," William said, trying to overcome the desperation in his voice. "I'm no spy. I'm a clerk for Deshon and Yarrington, African traders, right here on India Wharf! That's our office. I live in Boston! With my mother."

"Sure, sure, you're just an honest schoolboy who goes around lighting signals by accident when an enemy ship is creeping into Boston Harbor!"

"You're all wrong!" William said earnestly. "Let me get my mother! Get the principal of the English High School! I just graduated a month ago. I'm no spy!"

"Whyn't you in the Northern Army then, a big boy like you?"

"I won't be eighteen until next month. Ma says I got to wait until I'm twenty. Until I'm drafted."

"Bet you memorized all them things to say when you got caught. Come along. We'll take you to the Major."

He tried to protest, but the men seized his arms. They hurried him down the long dark cavern of India Wharf. One

[17

of the men sniffed appreciatively at the stacks of musty bales just unloaded from the *Helen,* the African schooner. "Must've cracked open a couple of barrels of rum over that stuff," he muttered.

There was a crowd of men swarming excitedly around the big cannon poised awkwardly at the end of the wharf jutting out into the harbor. A short, stocky man was silhouetted against the sky, looking out to sea as though he were peering over the breastworks of a fort. His uniform gleamed with newness. He stormed around and faced the confusion.

"Up with the barrel! Up, I say! Blast it all, men, you shoot the cannon at that elevation, you'll blow the wharf right out from under our feet! Up! Up with it!"

"Major! Major Johnson!"

"Don't bother me."

"Major, we got a spy! Young fellow here, giving signals to that Johnny Reb ship."

"It's a lie," William said. But his voice was hardly more than a whisper. He could feel himself drawing away from all the excitement. In his mind, he was on his hands and knees crawling through the marshes of Nahant, seeking the tiny things that moved beneath the surface of the stagnant water.

"A spy?" The little Major stopped prancing. He placed his hand on the scabbard that encased a long sword swinging from his waist. He advanced cautiously on William.

"Good work, men," Major Johnson said briefly. "We've been warned to watch for these spies. Good work. Want to get a good look at him before we hang him."

He wheeled around suddenly, flourishing his sword. "Back to the cannon, you others. Back, all of you! Want us to be surprised and slaughtered in our tracks just because we got to hang a spy? Back to your posts! On guard!"

The men scurried back to the huge cannon. The three captors and the Major hurried William inside the pier shed. The heavy door creaked shut.

"Strike a light. It won't show through that door."

"Wait a minute. What's that noise?"

"Confederates! They're under the wharf!"

They strained in silence. All about them was a thin chittering, an eerie sound of light, fairy feet.

The Major snorted. "Rats. Hundreds of them."

There was a sound of a sword being withdrawn from its scabbard. "All right," the Major whispered, "strike a light. And don't move!"

Suddenly the inside of the pier flared with yellow light. Transfixed in the brilliant glow, five rats stood poised on a dusty wooden beam immediately above the Major's head. The sword flashed through the air. The severed body of a rat tumbled to the ground.

The Major smiled in satisfaction. He wiped the blade of the sword on a bale of jute, and slipped it back into its scabbard. "Used to practice on the farm," he said modestly, "with a pitchfork. Got 'em every time."

He cleared his throat. "Light that lantern. Let's get finished with this spy business. We'll give him a fair, fast trial. Somebody got a rope handy?"

"Here's the code book he was going to toss overboard, Major. And we saw him give those signals, plain as can be. Three times."

"I was looking for something," William interrupted.

"Keep quiet. You wait till the Major asks you to speak."

Major Johnson held the book gingerly in the palm of his hand. He mouthed the words of the title as he pronounced it aloud. "In-ver-te-brata of Massachusetts. Hum. . . ." He

[19

thumbed through the book, peering at the illustrations. "Looks like he's got a sketch of every fortification in the state of Massachusetts."

William shook his head. "Major, your finger is on a drawing of the nervous system of a nemertinean."

"Quiet. I tell you, men," the Major said abruptly, "this what you did, capturing this spy, might just have saved the whole of Boston! You're going to get a medal for this night's work, mark my words!" He spun about to William. "You got anything to say before we hang you?"

"I'm not a spy," William answered doggedly. "I'm an American, a northerner. I love my country just as much as any of you."

"Well," the Major said as he held his thumb upright and squinted at the beam overhead, "I'll try to remember what you said, son. Maybe those words'll go down in a history book sometime. You, Carty, throw the rope over the rafter."

"Major, before we do it, ask him does he know anything about the Confederate's plans for the invasion?"

The Major rubbed his cheek thoughtfully. "This Captain Tonso McCrae, the Confederate skipper of the raider *Shannon*—he a friend of yours?"

"Never heard of him."

"Oh, come, mister, they ain't no man alive in the North who ain't heard of Tonso McCrae!" The Major reached for his sword in a gesture of anger. "Why, just saying that fellow's name is enough to make my blood boil! Sinking all them northern merchants ships, everyone of them unarmed and doing nobody no harm!"

"I never heard of him," William repeated dully. What was the use of talking? To die now, so foolishly, when there was so much to live for! So much to learn and love! So many investigations to make, so much research to do! But the words kept coming, "I don't get a chance to read much about the war news. I work every day and many nights like tonight, and the Museum, and field trips for specimens . . ." his voice trailed off. There was no need for explanations. If they were going to hang him, let them get it over with. He thought of his mother at home, alone, and of his father, across the world in the mission fields of India.

The Major shook his head sorrowfully. "No use trying to cover up, son. Just convinces me more'n ever I'm doing right hanging you. You and that Tonso McCrae just about the same age, too." He shook his head in envy, looking out beyond the closed door toward the open sea. "Nineteen years old, that McCrae, and him practically the whole Southern Navy!"

He leaned confidentially toward William. "We got word he's leading that flotilla of Confederate ships into this harbor this very night!" He patted his sword in a confident gesture. "What I wouldn't give if that Captain Tonso McCrae was standing in front of me, instead of you! What I wouldn't give!"

"Got his friend, Major, and that's pretty good," the volunteer, Carty, said excitedly.

"That's true, Carty. We'll get along with our business."

"Major Johnson!" a voice called from the outer darkness.

"What is it? How can a man do his work with all these interruptions?"

"Them Harvard boys is here! Come down to help us save Boston! Got one of their professors as a leader."

"Send him in. And shut that door fast! Don't let the enemy see this light. We'll be blown right into the Bay."

A slight, bespectacled man, his intelligent face fringed with a dark beard, ducked through the doorway. He held out his hand to the Major. "I'm Professor Louis Agassiz, Comparative Zoology, Harvard University. We heard the call for assistance and organized a group of volunteers!"

The Professor looked sharply over Major Johnson's shoulder. His eyes darted to the rope dangling downward over William. "What's going on here?"

"Just in time to witness a hanging, Professor. Caught us a spy."

"Caught your foot in your mouth, my dear Major," the Professor replied quietly.

"How dare you, sir! This boy's a spy! He was seen signaling to the enemy out in the Bay. He's got his code book on him, just jammed full of the fortifications in the state of Massachusetts!"

"This book," Professor Agassiz answered evenly, "is written by a friend of mine, Professor A. A. Gould. I loaned it personally to that boy standing there."

"You did?"

"I did."

Major Johnson fidgeted with his sword. "The boy said he was lighting a match to hunt for snails."

"Of course. This is William Healey Dall, one of the most promising young scientists in the Boston area. I'd be very much disappointed if he were to pass by one chance to add to his very great knowledge of invertebrata."

William smiled gratefully at Professor Agassiz.

"Inverte—what's the word, Professor?"

"Perhaps I should say snails, Major."

"Maybe snails to you, but it's secret military information to me. And I'm not letting that boy walk out into the night to give more signals to them enemy ships that's aiming to invade Boston!"

"Major. I give you my word as a scholar. . . ."

"You give me nothing, Professor. I'm in charge of the defense of Boston Harbor. I'm taking no orders from any college professor. Now you take your students and mount guard over the far end of the wharf. By heavens, don't try to interfere with me no more! Get along, sir!"

"Major Johnson, Major Johnson! They're coming. The Confederates are coming! You can see the sails! They're creeping up!"

The wild, terrified yell echoed through the vast pier shed. Major Johnson started. "I've got to go to my post," he said solemnly. "I've got to defend Boston." He looked uncertainly from William back to the thin, dark-bearded man beside him. "I leave the prisoner in your charge, Professor. I'll have him hung when the battle is over."

He ran through the open door to the shouting men who swarmed around the cannon.

William stepped over to Professor Agassiz. "I can't thank you. I can't. . . ." He choked on his words.

"Say nothing, William. This will all be forgotten in the morning. Everyone is excited, nervous. Foolish things are bound to happen. Come with me. I want you to be with our group of students."

They hurried outside and joined the twelve young men who moved in the shadows.

"Professor," one of them called, "I don't think it's a fake attack! You can really see a ship out there! She's moving in slowly. Watch when that cloud goes away from the moon."

The cloud drifted away. Slowly, almost like a shadow above the water, the dark outline of a sail took form. The students leaned far over the coping, as though anxious to swim out and engage the enemy. Two jumped high on the wooden bit. They balanced precariously while they strained through the darkness.

"Yippee! We're going to have a real fight!"

"Quiet down there! Pass the word. Quiet!"

A weird assortment of weapons passed among the students. A rusty pistol was thrust into William's hand. He stared at it in wonder, marveling at its age.

"Quiet!" A voice bellowed. "We're getting ready to fire the cannon! The Major wants absolute quiet!"

Dimly, in the darkness, they could make out the intense activity around the cannon. The short, busy figure of Major Johnson was seen peering along the barrel that was almost bigger around than he.

William sucked in his breath. He thought of the old, rotten planking beneath the cannon. It would feel the full shock of the recoil from the monstrous relic rolled down from the Arsenal.

Major Johnson stabbed the finger of his left hand into his ear. With the other hand he took a lighted taper and held it close to the fuse hole. He was trembling violently. Just before the lighted taper touched, the Major called, "Men, we fight now for the honor of our beloved city!"

His right hand dipped. The taper touched. There was a crackling hiss, then Boooo—OOOO—mmmm!

The cannon leaped convulsively. It belched smoke and flame. There was a whistling sound as the shot roared out to sea. Then came a crack of splintering wood, and a loud splash.

"Hurray! We've hit her! She's a goner!"

"Quiet, you fool! The cannon's fallen through the wharf into the water. We didn't hit nothing. Somebody fish out the Major!"

24]

William held his hand over his hand, trying to smother the fierce fit of giggling that swept over him.

Out in the stream there was a roar of angry voices.

"Ahoy, the shore, there! Lay off, you idiots! This is an American ship, the *India Queen*, inbound from Calcutta. Can't a man tie up to his Company's wharf without getting his ship blown to bits by a bunch of make-believe soldiers?"

Major Johnson, thoroughly soaked, looked about. "The *India Queen*! My Uncle Nathaniel's skipper of that ship! I shot my own uncle!" He grasped his sword and swung about in a wide, dripping circle. "Who started this false rumor about an invasion? Who's the man responsible? Bring him to me."

He spied William and came for him. "Young fellow, is it true? Is that the *India Queen*? Isn't she one of Deshon and Yarrington's fleet?"

"Of course, Major," William replied evenly. "She was reported early this morning becalmed off Race Point. That's why I was working late tonight—to pass the word to the owners when she was warping in."

"You knew that all the time, and you let the city of Boston get into a turmoil over this crazy rumor, that, that. . . ." The Major sputtered into silence. Then he spun about and yelled at his men. "All of you, back to your homes. We'll be needing no more volunteers this night!"

"Boston is saved," one of the students yelled.

"I'll have no insolence from you Harvard boys," the Major snapped. "There might come a time when you'll be mighty thankful. . . ."

"Ahoy, the India Wharf," a voice called from the ship, now very close, "is it safe to throw over a heaving line?"

"Throw and be danged, Uncle Nate," the Major yelled

back into the darkness. "Next time show your lights like a civilized ship. You won't cause so much trouble!"

A thin line snaked through the air. The heavy knotted end thumped to the wooden planking of the wharf. William leaped forward and hauled on the rope vigorously. Behind the thin line a heavy hawser came dripping through the water. Slowly the big sailing ship eased in to the wooden coping.

Professor Agassiz came to William.

"Come to the University tomorrow, my friend," he said. "I'll have good news for you."

"You've heard from the Smithsonian Institution about the specimens I sent?"

"Perhaps—but that is not what I had in mind. Professor Gould has presented your name to the council of the Boston Society of Natural History. You have been accepted. There is work waiting for you, scientific work."

William sucked in his breath. He tried to speak. He choked back his words when his lips started to tremble and betrayed his emotion. Finally he found the right words. "All my life, Professor Agassiz, I have wanted an opportunity like this. All my life."

The Professor cleared his throat. "And for our part, perhaps we have been waiting a long time for a young man like you, with your enthusiasm, your knowledge, your love of natural history. You will give much to science—perhaps more than science will give to you." He turned away abruptly. "Come see me in the morning."

William watched him go. He wanted to call out his joy. But there was a voice from the ship that hailed him.

"William! William! Here, here by the ship's rail!"

The boy turned about and looked hard in the darkness. Then, in the soft glow of the lights that were springing up, he saw a kind face beaming and hands outstretched in love.

"Father, you've come back!"

"For a visit only, my son. The mission fields of India still need me."

William leaped over the low wooden rail and embraced his father. The older man sighed deeply in satisfaction. Then he held his son at arm's length and looked at him tenderly.

"I am going back to India very soon, William. And this time, you will be with me. I, to my missionary work, you to become a tea merchant. The arrangements are made. Everything is settled and waiting for our return."

"Father . . . Father . . ."

"What is it, William? Why are you shaking your head? Why are you crying?"

CHAPTER THREE

A sticky heat enveloped Boston the next day as William walked by his father. The Reverend Charles Henry Appleton Dall, only forty-seven years old, was sober and solemn in the long, black linen cloak that hung nearly to the ground.

"Father, I just can't go to India. I want to be here, near Professor Agassiz and the Museum. I'm working on so many collections . . . there are so many specimens I've just begun to. . . ." His voice trailed off.

The Reverend Dall seemed scarcely to hear. He was a saintly character, and looking at him, William had the feeling his father was talking to God.

Suddenly he was conscience-stricken. How could he hurt his father this way? Why shouldn't he turn his back on scientific work and go off to India to become a tea merchant? Anything, anything to avoid hurting this kindly man who walked so solemnly by his side.

The Reverend Dall stroked his beard thoughtfully. His gentle eyes looked fondly at the ivy-covered walls of Harvard University. "So very different from India," he murmured. "So very different. What was it you were saying, William?"

The boy shook his head. He bit back the words that stormed to his lips. Then he smacked his right hand vigorously in the palm of his hand. "Sometimes," he blurted out, "I think I'm an idiot!"

"An idiot? A Dall, an idiot?"

"I mean—thinking I'm a scientist. Just because I'm interested in little things that most people ignore, or step on, or hate, or run away from! Sometimes, when I get down on my hands and knees and explore in the swamps, I've seen people watching me. They think I'm crazy!"

The Reverend Dall placed his arm around William's shoulder. The boy looked gratefully at his father, then followed the pointing cane in the older man's hand. It pointed to the aging cluster of buildings in the yard.

"Do not be ashamed of your love for little things, my son," Rev. Dall said quietly. "This institution we love, Harvard University, is an example. It was already old in wisdom when this country was born. And it has grown to real greatness through the years because men have not sought fame in great projects here, but knowledge in little ones."

A baby sparrow, gone too soon from a nest beneath the eaves, fluttered down and came to rest on the outstretched cane.

The Reverend Dall had graduated from Harvard twenty-six years before, in 1837. Afterwards he had attended Divinity School and had been ordained an evangelist. Because he was driven by a desire to help the poor and the unfortunate, he had gone first to Saint Louis where he had conducted a school for poor boys and girls. Afterwards he went to Baltimore where he gave himself unstintingly for the same services under Unitarian auspices.

On a visit to nearby Washington, D. C., he had met Caroline Wells Healey, a teacher in Miss English's Female Seminary,

[29

and the two had married. A year later, on August 21, 1845, William was born in Boston, Massachusetts.

The boy's earliest recollections were of journeys to seemingly distant places. He remembered dimly a chugging train ride to Portsmouth, New Hampshire, a city that faced out to sea. And he remembered standing on the deck of a lake steamer as it crossed Lake Ontario for the family's short stay in Canada.

Through the years he had lost track of his father's precise movements during that restless time. When he was not quite ten years old, the family had returned to Boston. A few months later the elder Dall was appointed by the American Unitarian Association as its missionary to India. William had stood by the water front, watching the sailing ship disappear, not quite understanding why his father was dropping from his life. The Reverend Dall had felt that it was necessary to leave his family back in the United States.

And so, to William, his father had become only a faint memory, a writer of letters on thin, musty-smelling paper. Stronger were his recollections of the hardships he and his mother knew during the years when he attended the Allen Brothers School, the Brimmer School, and, finally, the English High School. He was deeply attached to his mother, yet he feared her sharp tongue. Mrs. Dall was a scholar, strictly puritanical, and frankly outspoken, given to critical remarks that carried more sting than she had intended.

During all his school years William was constantly reminded of the struggle his mother endured to keep the family intact. Shy and reserved, he felt as though he were peering over a fence, watching his mother in the daily struggle to add to the family income by teaching and writing.

Perhaps, he mused, it was his loneliness, separated by half

a world from his missionary father, and by a wide gulf of anxiety from his mother, that had turned him to studying the little creatures in life.

He was prodded from his reverie by his father's gentle voice. "I have found happiness with my work in India, my son. It would be wrong for me to deny you happiness in yours. You do not need to come to India. You have my permission to continue your scientific studies."

"Thank you, father."

The Reverend Dall nodded his head. "You already know Professor Agassiz here at the University. Come, I will introduce you to others of my friends who may be able to help you."

Late the next afternoon William slid from his high bookkeeping stool, walked across the uneven floor, and knocked at Mr. Yarrington's office door.

"Come in," the gruff voice responded.

"Mr. Yarrington," William said, "I want to . . . I want to resign."

Piercing blue eyes transfixed him. He could feel his knees knocking. "Resign, eh?" Mr. Yarrington demanded. "Let me tell you something, young Dall, office boys don't resign in this establishment—they quit or they're fired! Now if you're trying to tell me you're quitting. . . ."

"Sir," William said miserably, "all I'm trying to say is that I have an opportunity to do scientific work with Professor Agassiz at Harvard."

"Scientific work? Humph! Boys can't do scientific work. All they do in this office is spill ink and make wrong entries in ledgers." He rose ponderously and came around the desk. "Your father know about this, William? This scientific work of yours?"

William nodded. Mr. Yarrington weighed almost three hundred pounds. He stood over William like an enormous tree.

"Well, I'm surprised, that's what I am, surprised. A respectable man like the Reverend Dall allowing a son of his to . . . to. . . ." He shook his head and sighed. "Things is changing. Not like when I was a young fellow. People today don't know how to work. That's it," he said triumphantly, "people just don't know how to work!" He sighed again. "Well, for your father's sake, I won't put no obstacles in your way, although, mark my words, you'll be shiftless all your life." He smiled benignly. "Have one of the older clerks write a nice letter about your honesty, and I'll be glad to sign it. Good-by, William."

It was scarcely a month later that the *India Queen* dropped with the tide away from India Wharf. William Healey Dall lifted his hand in farewell to the figure at the stern. His father's black linen coat fluttered in the wind. Across the widening waters of Boston Bay an unspoken message passed between them.

Then each turned to the work of his heart.

With the help of Professor Agassiz, who was destined to be named as one of the greatest of American naturalists, William daily increased his knowledge of the little creatures that made up a world almost unnoticed by most humans.

In the few moments when he lifted his head from his eager study of mollusks, William could not reproach the outside world for seeming to be indifferent to the science of Mollusca.

The fury of the Civil War, deep into its second year, was mounting. The nation was tearing itself apart in bloody strife.

Always with the news of the battle, as victory and defeat seesawed across the nation, were the stories of the legendary

32]

Captain Tonso McCrae. While the news of the Confederate land victories began to ebb, the exploits of Tonso McCrae became bitter pills for the North to swallow. His ship, the *Shannon*, was like a will-o'-the-wisp. It was reported seen in every ocean of the world. McCrae hunted the merchants ships of the northern states with great ruthlessness. There was even an incredulous report that the *Shannon* had ventured far north into Arctic waters, shelling the few Yankee whalers that had ventured into those forbidden Russian areas.

"Get Tonso McCrae!" was the cry heard throughout the North. "Hang him!"

William listened in mild wonder, then returned to his study of the dog whelks and periwinkles, the blood starfish and the rock crabs in the waters surrounding Boston. He was fascinated by every tiny creature he dredged from the sea. Each movement was a challenge to his understanding. Each shell was an object of intense study, waiting to be named and catalogued.

But the war was so terrible and so overwhelming in its scope, that even science was threatened.

Professor Louis Agassiz called William into his study. His face was troubled. "The was is draining everything," he said soberly. "Our funds for research have been cut. We can't continue your work, William. There is no money to pay you."

"I'll work without pay! I can't stop now, Professor!"

Agassiz shook his head. "You are the only one to whom your mother can turn, William. She needs your help. Even more than science."

It was with a heavy heart that William trudged homeward, heedless of the dark storm clouds that were black over Boston. The newsboys on the streets were shouting a war extra.

"Tonso McCrae sinks Yankee ship off New York Harbor! Congress offers ten thousand dollars reward for the capture of McCrae, dead or alive!"

Why did they hate McCrae so, William wondered. This was war. Killing and being killed was expected. But not hatred.

His mother shed no tears over the loss of the research work with Professor Agassiz.

"Good riddance," she said briskly. "Perhaps now you'll turn your talents to something productive. There's money to be earned in these war days, William."

He smiled ruefully. His mother never could quite understand his love of mollusks. She eyed with suspicion the strange things he brought home in jars and stacked neatly on shelves in his bedroom. Yet he never ceased hoping that someday she would look upon "those squirmy little things!" with the same love and affection that he did.

He admired his mother greatly. She was worn, tired with the endless effort to preserve a home in Boston for her family while she continued daily with her teaching in the public school. There was always the wistful hope that in the future she might join her husband in his mission work in India. But until that day came, money was a prime necessity in the Dall household.

"Mother," William said, "I'm going to help."

She stiffened, then reached for her spectacles and put them on with a nervous gesture. "You're not running off and joining the Army after all I've said? You're just a boy, William, barely nineteen. Surely you can wait another year until you're drafted?"

"Yes, Mother. I promise. But I'm going to work for the railroad."

"The railroad?"

"The Reverend Collyer was at the University today. He suggested I accept a clerkship with the Illinois Central Railroad in Chicago."

"In Chicago—that's a thousand miles away!"

William nodded. He went to the door and looked far down to the sea, a faint blue streak beneath the dark clouds that had started to pour rain upon the grateful city. Already he was saying good-by to everything he loved.

He had the same feeling of depression, a feeling that the world he had loved was ended, when he crossed the state of Massachusetts by train. He felt no excitement at the new scenes that drifted behind. He stood alone in the stern of the ferry that brought him across the Hudson River to Albany, dispirited, and there was no feeling of elation when he climbed into the waiting New York Central train. He sat silently by the grimy windows.

The little train chuffed westward.

As though in a dream he looked out at the dry wheat fields of Ohio and Indiana. Everything was gone.

It was a sweltering hot day when he stepped from the shade of the terminal to the streets of Chicago. Newsboys, gasping for breath, were silent, holding aloft newspapers. Black headlines streamed across the front page: "Democratic Convention ends in Chicago. General McClellan nominated to run against Abraham Lincoln."

The date was August 29, 1864.

William started his work in the Land Office of the Illinois Central in a crowded building shoved down by the swamps bordering the lake. He tried as best as he could to help in the disposal of the vast railroad land holdings to the settlers crowding into the Mississippi Valley.

He went through the motions of his work, trying hard to be of service to his employers, trying to be worthy of the $27.50 he was receiving each month in salary.

But at noon, and again in the evening, he stepped across the shining railroad tracks, and walked by the swamps that shaped the borders of Lake Michigan. He walked alone on the beaches, his eyes scanning the tiny pools that remained when the tide ebbed outward.

This was his work, he thought. It always would be.

He was on his knees, scanning a piece of driftwood that might have sheltered some teredos, when a shadow, long in the afternoon sun, towered over him. He turned about slowly and smiled at the giant of a man who stood with his hands on his hips, looking down at him.

"Teredo navalis?" the stranger demanded.

"Teredo navalis," William answered, grinning. Here was a man who knew the language of mollusks.

The stranger thrust out his hand. "I'm Bob Kennicott. Academy of Science Museum here in Chicago. And you're William Dall? We had a letter from Professor Agassiz about you. How about coming over to meet Nason, Bannister—the rest of the gang? We've got specialists in anthropology, zoology, geology, botany; fine collection of meteorites—or we'll wrestle you for wooden nickels. Take your choice!"

There on the wet sands of Lake Michigan, the meeting of those two hands was the beginning of a friendship that was to last until death came to one in the Arctic four thousand miles away. It was William's initiation into the small scientific circle then existing in the prairie city of Chicago.

Although only in his late twenties, Bob Kennicott was already well-known as an explorer and a scientist. "We're all excited," he said at the Museum, "about this Western Union project."

William was ashamed to confess that he knew nothing of what Bob was saying. "Seemed all my waking moments centered around getting a complete set of Massachusetts Mollusca for Professor Agassiz back in Boston. Tell me about the Western Union project, please."

Bob Kennicott was all enthusiasm. "It's a telegraph line clear around the world—or most of it, anyhow. Surely you've heard of it?"

"Vaguely."

"Russia's stretching a line seven thousand miles across her own country and Siberia to the Bering Strait. Then there's to be a forty-mile cable beneath the Strait over to the North American continent. Western Union's already got a line across the United States and clear up to Portland. They have authorization to go north through British Columbia. Men are stringing the lines up there right now." He shook his head doubtfully. "Then comes the worst stretch of all."

"Where?" William asked.

"Across Russian America. Nineteen hundred miles. Absolute wilderness. Hardly a white man in the entire region—yet we're going to string a telegraph wire clear across the width of the country."

"You're part of the expedition?"

Kennicott nodded his head briefly. "I've been up in the Canadian coastal regions on an expedition for the Smithsonian Institution." He spun a globe representing the world. His strong fingers brought it to rest, his thumb on a large yellow spot well above the United States. "Charles Bulkley, the chief engineer of the entire project, wants me to take an exploration party north next spring. We're to map the best possible route for the line through Russian America."

He spun about and leaned over eagerly. "I want you as a member of my party, William. Will you come?"

William rose to his feet and moved away. He shook his head. Then he turned back to Kennicott, holding tight to the globe to steady himself. "Before I'm a scientist, Bob, I'm a citizen. By next spring I'll be wearing a uniform. I'll be off to war. Thanks for asking me."

He hurried from the room. He didn't want Bob to see the disappointment in his eyes.

Russian America. Alaska, the mysterious! Ten thousand secrets waiting to be uncovered by the first scientist lucky enough to dredge the ocean waters, the deep bays, and the muddy rivers of the unknown land!

To cover his disappointment, he buried himself in his work. He stopped his long walks along the beach. He ignored the invitations from Bob Kennicott to join the group at the Academy. He knew the discussions would center on the great expedition to Russian America. And he would not be able to take part.

He tried to pretend that the world of scientific knowledge he once had known no longer existed.

Yet it seemed the scientific world pursued him. Earlier, William's thirst for knowledge had been so great that he became expert not only in Mollusca but in other branches of science. He pored over geology books and became adept in reading the history of centuries in a careful examination of the rocks and sands about him. The Civil War was like a tremendous monster, devouring endless quantities of steel.

Spurred on by the demand, geological parties fanned out over Minnesota and Michigan, probing into the ground, seeking iron ore that could be converted to steel by the new Bessemer process. When William learned of a search to be conducted for iron ore deposits along the shores of Lake Superior in northern Michigan, he applied for a position, expounded on his knowledge of geologic formations, and was accepted.

All through the long, bitterly cold winter of 1864 he tramped over the frozen ground, his pick striking into the icy surface. At nineteen he was slender, almost slight; the bright, incisive mind of a grown man encased in the body of a boy not yet full-grown. He was reserved, and did not mix too readily with the others in the ore searching party. During the short daylight hours he kept to himself, his trained eyes alert to the signs that might betray the presence of the iron ore.

At night, alone, he stood outdoors, assaulted by the cold wind, and looked south to Chicago. He thought of the little group around the roaring fire in the Museum, discussing plans for the expedition to Russian America.

He left unanswered letters from Bob Kennicott. He was afraid to trust his feelings. He was afraid his pen would run away. His grief and disappointment might spill out upon the written pages.

In the spring of 1865, when the ice flows were grinding high on the shores of Lake Superior, one of his employers approached him.

"Dall, we've watched your work throughout the past winter. To be frank, we've been impressed. We need a man like you to manage our lead mine down in Missouri. I've been authorized to offer you a salary of two thousand dollars a year if you will accept."

"Two thousand dollars! I'm only making six hundred now!"

"We know that."

William could feel himself swaying. "Give me the night to think it over," he said. "I'll give you my answer in the morning."

Far into the night William sat by his window in the boardinghouse. A cold wind swept across the lake, and drifted snow against the glass. He looked upward at the moon breaking through the fleet of clouds that were sailing across the sky.

Two thousand dollars a year! A princely salary for a young man not yet turned twenty. There would be no scientific study, but there would be freedom from financial worry.

Yet, he knew he could not accept. He had known it almost from the first and was waiting only for the words to take proper form.

He took a sheet of paper, used a book for a desk, and wrote in a firm hand:

> Dear Sir:
> I regret I cannot accept your offer. I have made a firm resolve never to accept a position that will not permit me to pursue further scientific study.
> > Sincerely,
> > William Healey Dall

William started south to Chicago the following day. He searched for Bob Kennicott. "Bob," he said earnestly, "I'm going to Washington and join the Army. Someday, when I've finished my service, if you're still in Alaska—I'd like to come and join the expedition."

He shook his friend's hand hurriedly and almost ran down to the depot and the waiting train.

In Washington he spent two days walking slowly about the brick buildings of the Smithsonian Institution. He kept whispering "Hello" and "Good-by" to the priceless scientific treasures in the musty rooms. "When I come back from war," he murmured, "when I come back from war. . . ."

He stood reverently before a bronze plaque on which was inscribed the Smithsonian ideal:

For the Increase and Diffusion of Knowledge Among Men

A tall bearded man came from the shadows of the display cases and stood by his side.

"When I get back from the Army," William said impulsively, "I'm going to become a scientist! I am going to work for the Smithsonian and collect specimens from all over the world!"

The tall man nodded his head gravely. "Everyone will get back to the work he loves when the war is over. Everyone." He looked almost tenderly at William. "Is your father with the Union forces?"

"My father's a missionary, sir. He's giving his life to help the people of India."

The tall man bowed his head, as though he were praying. "One's life," he said, "is a small price to bring hope to an entire nation." He turned and started to walk off into the night. Then he paused, and turned back slowly. "Don't wait to get on with your scientific work, my son. The war is nearly over. There will be no more draft calls."

Then he turned and was gone.

William was still blinking in puzzlement when a policeman came behind him. The policeman leaned over and whispered: "My boy, you'll be telling your grandchildren how one night you talked with Abraham Lincoln, and him the President of the United States. That you did, boy. Come back here! You! Where are you going in such an all-fire hurry?"

"I'm sending a wire to Bob Kennicott! I'm off to Alaska!"

CHAPTER FOUR

"You idiot! I'll teach you to burn up things, you numskull! Take that! And that!"

"Help! He's murdering me! Help!"

The deep, gray-clouded calm hanging over the North Pacific Ocean was suddenly shattered by a series of yells, screams, and loud thumps on the deck of the bark, *Golden Gate*, pride of the Western Union fleet. Sailors slid down the rope from aloft, running midship. Heads popped out from the doors leading to the crews' quarters. Far aft the blue uniforms of officers showed as they hurried to see the cause of the commotion. Even the man at the wheel, startled at the screams and yells, forgot what he was doing and turned about. A sudden gust of wind seized the sails. The ship heeled dangerously.

"You, on the wheel! Mind what you're doing or I'll have you thrown overboard," Captain Charles M. Scammon bellowed through cupped hands. Then he turned to the milling throng below him. "What's going on aboard my ship?"

The white-coated cook stood over the mess boy, striking him repeatedly with a length of firewood. "Burn my calendar, you idiot! I'll teach you!"

He came down smartly with the wood on the seat of the mess boy's trousers. The boy screamed as though he had been run through with a bayonet. Several members of the crew lunged forward and seized the cook, wrestling the club away from his hands.

The cook opened and shut his mouth several times before the words came. He looked up at the Captain.

"This boy, Captain," he spluttered, "this idiot, this numskull——"

"I've heard that before," the Captain retorted. "What happened?"

"Sorry I hurt him, sir," the cook continued, wiping his hands on his apron, "but we been to sea for nearly three months, sir. Only way I could keep track of the days was to make notches in my wood calendar. And this fool put it in the stove and burned it up!"

"You're the idiot," the Captain said crisply. "Call Mr. Dall, the Acting Surgeon. Have him look after the boy. And don't let me catch you striking him again, or, by Harry, I'll have you tossed overboard!"

"I'm sorry, sir. I won't touch him. But my birthday—I can't tell am I forty-five or forty-six."

"What date is your birthday?" Carrying a small black case, the symbol of his office aboard the flagship, Dall asked the question as he brushed through the crowd and knelt by the sobbing mess boy.

"August 28, sir."

"Then you're forty-six years old. Bring me a pan of hot water."

"Forty-six! Forty-six!"

Back in the crowd a sailor shouted sarcastically, "Happy Birthday, cookie!" Then the crowd took up the song, "Happy Birthday, to yeeee—ewww! Happy Birthday to yeeeee—eew!"

The cook teetered about on the sloping deck, grinning happily.

"How about a good meal tonight for a change, cookie. It's your birthday!"

The cook nodded quickly, looking over his shoulder toward the Captain's quarters. Then he winked laboriously and hurried off.

William rubbed ointment on the bruised mess boy. "Not a thing wrong with you, son. That cook was yelling harder than he was hitting. What's your name?"

"Jonathan Benson."

"Glad to meet you, Jonathan. My name's William Healey Dall. First trip north?"

"Yes, sir."

"Well, we've got a lot in common. Come see me when you get finished working tonight. Maybe you'd want to help me mount my specimens."

"Gee, I'd like that Mr. Dall."

William grinned as he helped Jonathan to his feet. "Better not call me Mister. Makes me feel like an old man."

"But you're one of the officers, sir, and we're supposed to."

William looked around the almost empty deck. "All right, if people are around—Mister Dall. When it's just the two of us—William's the name. My cabin is next to the Captain's. Don't forget to come see me tonight."

William walked slowly to the very bow of the sailing ship. He leaned on the rail, listening to the soft slap of the wood against the water as the ship rose and fell on the waves. He looked dreamily at the rolling waters of the North Pacific. Overhead were dark, black-rimmed clouds threatening to spill rain at any moment. The sails were tight, almost bursting under the strain of the wind racing before the storm.

The *Golden Gate* had clawed its way northward from San Francisco, keeping in sight of the rugged coast line until the mountains of Baranof Island had been raised. Then the ship had turned east, picked its way through barrier islands, and anchored for ten days in the harbor of Sitka, capital of Russian America. Then they were off again, inching north and westward as they aimed for a pin point in the rolling waters, Unimak Pass in the Aleutian Islands.

The first drops of rain fell, but William continued standing, face to the wind. Beyond Unimak Pass would be the Bering Sea, and far to the left Siberia, where the telegraph line was waiting to be connected with America. To the right, hidden in the distance and the rain, was Russian America where the bulk of the exploration was still to be completed before the mammoth project linking the entire world was completed.

"Penny for your thoughts, Mr. Acting Surgeon."

William turned about. "Bob! I was just thinking how lucky I am to be part of the Expedition. It's the greatest thing ever happened to me. I'll never be able to thank you enough."

"Forget it," Bob Kennicott replied, leaning on the rail by William. "Just figure how I can discover the junction between the Kwikhpak and the Yukon rivers—and I'll be well repaid."

"What's making that so difficult, Bob?"

Kennicott sketched a map on the moisture-covered handrail. "It's like the Missouri River and the Mississippi, William. We know both the Yukon and the Kwikhpak make a circle around the interior of Alaska. I explored the headwaters of the Yukon four years ago when I was in British Columbia. We're sure the Kwikhpak empties up there in the Bering Sea. Most of us think the Yukon drains into the Arctic, but we're not sure, and it's not important. What we're trying to find out is the spot where they come close so we can lead our survey lines from the Yukon to the Kwikhpak, and head west to the Bering Sea." He shook his head. "It's not going to be easy. We'll probably be the first white men ever to explore the Yukon Basin."

"But it'll be fun!" William said.

Bob Kennicott grinned slightly. "Fun—and work." He looked over the rolling green water. "Captain tells me we should pick up Unimak Island tomorrow morning. If we have a favorable wind we should slip through the Pass during daylight to reach the Bering, and another week should have us unloading on the beach at Saint Michael's."

"You're tired, Bob," William said, looking anxiously at his friend, the director of all scientific work for the expedition. "Is there anything I can do to help?"

Kennicott passed his hand wearily across his face. "So many things a man has to think of, William. Supplies, weather, hiring native guides, making arrangements for the vessels to come in the spring——" He shook his head and then suddenly put his arm about William's shoulder. "Thank goodness we have you along to collect specimens for the Smithsonian! If they depended on me, I'd have nothing to send back but telegraph poles! Tell me, William, how many specimens have you sent back in these past six months since you joined us?"

William grinned. "I'm losing track. There were fifty-three hundred I shipped back from San Francisco after that trip across the peninsula at Nicaragua. And I've got hundreds I gathered during that ten-day stop at Sitka. And Captain Scammon says he may be able to put me ashore for a few hours on Unimak Island——"

"Wait!" Bob Kennicott threw up his hands in mock despair.

"Won't be any room left aboard this ship for supplies if you keep loading up with scientific specimens! You're a one-man expedition alone!" Suddenly he stopped and looked anxiously to the distant horizon.

"Thought I saw a sail out there," he muttered.

"What's wrong with that?" William demanded. "The ship would be southbound to San Francisco. It would take our mail back."

"Not if it's the ship I think it is," Bob replied.

"What do you mean?"

"We got the news in Sitka. Captain Scammon and I. We didn't want anyone to know about it for fear of panic. Captain Tonso McCrae is still loose up in these northern Pacific waters. The war's been over four months; Lincoln has been assassinated—and Tonso McCrae still doesn't know a thing about it! He's still at war and will be until we get word to him. Hope he doesn't blow any of our ships out of the water before we get a chance to tell him how things have changed."

"Tonso McCrae! But . . ." William started to say.

Kennicott didn't hear. He turned and walked away, his head bowed. He was only twenty-nine, but already the terrible strain of conducting the greatest man-made effort to conquer a new land was beginning to take its toll.

That night Jonathan Benson knocked timidly on William's cabin door. His eyes opened wide when he looked inside the tiny cabin. "Gosh, Mr. Dall, William—you don't have room to turn around. The place is full of bugs!"

"Sea invertebrates, Jonathan," William corrected, pointing to the glass vials and widemouthed bottles. "Those I collected on the beaches around Sitka. I've got to get them ready in case we meet a southbound vessel heading for San Francisco. Here's what I'd like you to do."

Patiently he demonstrated to Jonathan the method of preparing the specimens, the sea urchins, the bright red anemones and mussels, together with barnacles, limpets, chitons, snails, starfishes, hermit crabs, and other types of tiny life he had gathered at the edge of the sea.

"You're handling history, Jonathan," William said earnestly. "This is the very first time anyone has made a scientific collection of the invertebrate of Alaska."

"Gosh," Jonathan said, wrinkling his nose, "they look like brown spinach."

William smiled and turned back to his collection.

He was up before the gray light of day the next morning as Captain Scammon anxiously steered the bark closer and closer to Unimak Island. Suddenly the Captain grunted in satisfaction and pointed ahead. "There's Smoking Moses," he said. "Mt. Shishaldin. Keep looking, you can see a big ring of smoke. Active volcano."

Somewhere behind the ever-present storm clouds, the sun was threatening to break through. In the grim gray light, William could see the perfect cone of Mt. Shishaldin towering into the air, a ring of smoke drifting over it. Unimak Island itself and all the little islands that made treacherous the Pass to the Bering Sea were a dull, shaggy brown with no trees. Shriveled grasses covered the lonely islands.

As they neared the wide mouth of the Pass, the wind veered to the north, and the sails flapped dangerously. Captain Scammon snorted in disgust. "Just what I was afraid of. We'll have to beat our way through. No telling when we'll get to the Bering side. Mr. Mate!" he called loudly, "get the men aloft! With a bit of luck the current will drift us through the Pass. Make it lively!"

William looked hopefully at the Captain. Then a small boat was put over the side.

"You, Mr. Dall," the Captain said shortly, "get your collecting gear and climb into the boat. The Mate will put you ashore at Scotch Cap. Tonight, before dark, we'll pick you up at Cape Sarichef on the Bering side of the Pass. Get along, now. Don't keep the Mate waiting."

William almost tumbled over the side in his eagerness.

"Wait!" a voice called. Bob Kennicott came running up in the half darkness. He handed over a Sharps carbine. "You've got to take this with you, William. I can't have you ashore unarmed. No telling what you might run into."

William made a face as he accepted the rifle. It was the last thing he wanted in the miles of tramping and exploration that waited for him ashore on the lonely island. But he said nothing. He settled back in the stern, eyes to the bleak island that loomed ahead. As soon as the keel grated on the rocky beach, he leaped ashore and turned to say good-by. But the boat had already pulled away, lifting and falling on the swells as it headed back to the becalmed *Golden Gate.*

Suddenly William felt lonely. He wondered if it had been wise to leave the others. Then a sudden movement in the waters by his feet made him look downward. He dropped to his knees, exclaiming in delight. "White Natica!" he whispered. In the palm of his hand he held the moon snail, so like those he had seen scores of times on the New England beaches. At once he forgot his loneliness, the *Golden Gate,* the small fears of the strange island.

The hours sped by as he worked his way steadily along the rocky beach. From time to time he moved back inland, following the wet shore line of an unnamed creek that tumbled down from the mountain to meet the salt sea. He pried up flat stones, and peered into moist, dark places where mollusks might be hiding. He had his small spring forceps continually in hand, so well versed in their use that they became like a pair of dexterous fingers. From his hip pocket extended a stick to which was attached a cheesecloth net twelve inches in diameter. He beat the coarse grasses with a practiced gesture so that the hidden creatures fell captive into the cheesecloth. He inverted the net over a wide piece of paper, picked out his prize captives, and placed them carefully in a small tin mustard box.

In his other hip pocket was a garden trowel that he used for digging into the moist ground and the wave-washed sand. From time to time he exclaimed in delight at the new discoveries he unearthed.

Every shell that he uncovered and identified added a tiny stroke of confirmation to all living things since the very beginning of time. The shell itself was of little importance, but the fragment of knowledge that it imparted, added to that already known, became of the greatest importance.

Far out in the Pass the *Golden Gate* inched steadily forward. But William paid little attention. He was completely engrossed in the immense numbers of minute creatures that teemed by the millions on this deserted island seemingly at the outer end of the world. He was the first American scientist ever to reach out his hand and give a name to the crustaceans, worms, mollusks, and echinoderms feeding in the algae and seaweed of that Aleutian shore. He was a new scientist in a new world, a man scarcely out of boyhood who stood on the verge of one of the greatest scientific careers of all time.

There was a noise of rocks clattering behind him, and he spun about. Jonathan Benson, cold and shivering, came around the corner of a large, weed covered boulder.

[51

"Jonathan! How did you ever get ashore! What's wrong?"

The boy tried to speak. His lips quivered, and suddenly he sank to his knees, weeping bitterly. "That cook," he cried, "he hit me again. I couldn't stand it. This morning, I slipped over the side and swam to shore. I don't ever want to go back to the ship. I'm going to live on this island by myself—just like Robinson Crusoe!"

William listened in astonishment. "You couldn't have picked a more rugged island. Hungry?"

Jonathan nodded eagerly. "Starving."

William dug into his pocket and pulled out a sandwich. He shared it with the young boy who wolfed it eagerly. "Next we'll build a little fire and get those clothes dried. You know how to build a fire?"

Jonathan shook his head dolefully. "We had servants at home in San Francisco. They built the fire."

William lifted his eyebrows. "Robinson Crusoe had a slight advantage over you. Hop along the beach there and see if you can find some dry twigs beneath those windfalls."

After he was thoroughly dry and his hunger satisfied, Jonathan was full of determination. "Here," he said, "let me carry the carbine. That's one thing I learned to do. I can hit a bull's-eye at a hundred yards. Want to see?"

"Never mind," William said hastily. "You fire that gun and we'll have the whole ship tumbling ashore, trying to find out what's going on. Let's get going. I've got work to do."

Mile after mile they tramped along the shore line, always with the *Golden Gate* silhouetted against the brown of Akutan Island on the far side of the Pass. Once the sun broke through the storm clouds, and they marveled at the snowy conical peak of Mt. Shishaldin, wreathed in lazy smoke from the volcano that churned within. William walked close to the water's edge, his eyes alert for the small starfishes, sea worms, and jellyfishes that were so abundant in the long strands of giant kelp that rose and fell with the sweeping of the sea. He took off his shoes, rolled up his trousers, and walked the submerged reefs, or trod carefully through the sandy bottom. The water, only a few hundred miles south of the Arctic Circle, was cold but bearable. "The Japan Current sweeps through the Aleutian Islands," he explained to the curious Jonathan. "That's why I'm not freezing."

"The Japan Current must have been flowing the wrong way this morning when I was swimming," Jonathan retorted. "I nearly froze to death." He looked anxiously toward the *Golden Gate*. "Guess they won't ever let me back on board that ship again. Guess I'll just have to stay on this island and starve to death. They'll be sorry, when they come back and find me——" His lips started to quiver.

"Don't worry, Jonathan. We'll think of something. Let's keep moving."

William kept peering into the rocky crevices. He had heard that the octopus was particularly abundant in the Aleutian chain. He leaned over a flat rock. "There's one," he whispered. Scarcely five feet across, its eight arms moving like seaweed, the unsuspecting octopus waited for the incoming tide.

"Mr. Dall! Mr. Dall! Mr. Dall! Behind you!"

The scream of terror made William spin around. Out of the brown, dried grasses by the water's edge a huge monster slowly reared, its mouth wide, uttering a full-throated cry of rage. The bear's outspread paws waved slowly in the air, razor-sharp talons outlined against its brown fur.

William started to run wildly along the beach, stumbling

and falling. Behind him the massive animal loped forward, his mouth opening and shutting in howls of rage.

There was the sudden crack of a rifle. The bear stopped as though it had been struck by a pole. It hesitated, wavering from side to side, then slumped to the ground. Jonathan came running. He held the barrel beneath the small ear of the bear, pulled the trigger again. The huge animal kicked convulsively, then was still.

William came back. He was pale and shaking. "Thank you for saving my life, Jonathan," he said quietly, and held out his hand. "I think Robinson Crusoe would have found you a might handy partner to have around."

"What's going on here! You, boy, what are you doing on this island? Why aren't you back there peeling. . . . Holy Smokes! Look at that bear!"

William and Jonathan turned around. A boat had pulled to the beach. The sailors were streaming ashore, whistling in astonishment at the dead monster stretched upon the beach. The Mate kept blinking his eyes. "Didn't know you could shoot like that, Mr. Dall. Takes an expert hunter——"

"I didn't shoot him. Jonathan, here did it."

The Mate looked at Jonathan with new respect. "Son, that's nearly a ton of fresh meat waiting for the crew. You've been wasting your time in the galley. We've got to find a new job for you, keeping us supplied with meat for the rest of the voyage." He put his arm around the boy's shoulder. "You, Thompson," he called, "you've done this sort of work before. Cut up that bear, and get it loaded so we can take it back to the *Golden Gate*. Mind you don't hurt that skin. That's for Jonathan, here."

Back aboard the ship there was great rejoicing when the thick slabs of bear meat were hoisted aboard. The only unhappy person was the cook. He kept glancing furtively at Jonathan. "A boy, that's what he is. Nothing but a boy who got a lucky shot at a bear. Humph! Anybody could do that."

"Start making motions with that bear meat, cook. I'll detail you three extra men so we can have a feast all around," ordered the Mate.

"You going to let me have that mess boy for help?" the cook asked, licking his lips in anticipation.

"Of course not. He's eating with the officers tonight."

As though there were no end to good luck, the wind suddenly freshened and the *Golden Gate* was safely on the Bering Sea side of the chain. The ship heeled confidently into the long rolling waves that swept the shallow waters, clicking off the miles that yet remained before they would reach Saint Michael's.

With each passing day William became more excited. He climbed the rigging, straining to look ahead and to the right, trying to pick up his first glimpse of the mainland of Russian America. There had been rumors that the United States was negotiating to buy the entire northland from Russia, but most people dismissed the thought. "Why," they said, "this country of ours is less than one hundred years old. We've stretched from one ocean to another—and now you want us to reach into the Arctic for more land? What good is that icebox up there?"

William knew its worth. It was a vast, unexplored region waiting for the first scientist to come ashore and dig into its secrets. And it would be he, William Healey Dall, who would answer that challenge.

"There it is!" he yelled. "There's the mainland!" He pointed eagerly to the tiny spot on the horizon.

"For heaven's sake, Mr. Dall," Captain Scammon called

up to him, "get down out of that rigging and leave the sailing of this ship to my crew. That's not the mainland. It's Nunivak Island."

Red-faced, William climbed slowly down. Bob Kennicott came alongside, chuckling. "Don't pay any attention to the Captain, William," he said. "It's been a long, hard voyage, and he's naturally nervous. We're getting very close, though. When we're past Cape Mohican on Nunivak Island, we'll start bending to the east and enter Norton Sound. A few more days will see us in."

"Bob, I can hardly wait," William said excitedly. "It's going to be the greatest adventure of my life. To think of going into the Interior, up the Yukon River, and with you as leader! You've been there before—you know everything—you'll be able to show me."

Kennicott was suddenly silent. He started to speak, then turned on his heel, and walked away. William watched him go, puzzled. "He's not feeling well," he thought. "Bob's sick. He's been under a strain, too, just like Captain Scammon."

As they kept bearing northward the air became appreciably colder, and the waves started tumbling about, tossing the *Golden Gate* like a cork. William fought down the temptation of seasickness. He stayed on deck, always searching for the mainland.

On September thirteen, a sailor in the bow suddenly turned about and called through cupped hands, "Land, ho, off the starboard bow!"

The bark anchored a quarter mile out from the rocky coast of Saint Michael's Island. Small boats put out quickly, swarming around the newcomer. William watched, swept up in the excitement of the arrival. Cargo was passed over to the smaller boats which made a quick run into the dangerous beach, unloaded, and came out again like swarms of ants groping close to a mound of sweets.

William tried to make himself useful. He hoisted cargo aloft from the holds, lowered it to the waiting boats, lashed it securely for the journey to the shore. He kept looking over his shoulder, waiting for Bob Kennicott to tell him to go ashore with the next load. Bob Kennicott, busy with a thousand and one details, avoided him.

Jonathan Benson was one of the first to leave. He came running along the deck, his arms loaded with gear, stumbling and falling as he headed for the rail.

"Let me help you, Jonathan," William said. He lifted off the roll of blankets and reached for the rifle.

"Not that, Mr. Dall," the young boy said hurriedly. "That's my badge of office. I'm going to be the hunter for the first river party—did you know that?"

"No. I didn't. I hope I'm with you, Jonathan. I'm sure everyone in your group will eat well."

"You will be with us, won't you? I just took it for granted——"

"I'll be with you. Just waiting to hear from Bob Kennicott. I'll see you ashore."

Finally the last crate of supplies was lifted from the *Golden Gate* and lowered to a small boat alongside. William was on fire with eagerness. He had his gear ready. He had given instructions to the First Mate on the safe delivery of the crated specimens that were to return to San Francisco. He kept looking impatiently to the low, treeless coast line, wondering just when he would be able to set foot ashore and start his explorations. He looked about.

"Where's Bob Kennicott?" he demanded of the Mate.

"In his cabin. Sent word he wants to see you."

William ran to the cabin. He thrust his head inside, all smiles. "I'm ready, Bob! Will we be going ashore in this boat that's waiting?"

"Come in, William."

William stepped over the threshold. Something was wrong. "What is it, Bob?"

Kennicott shook his head. He smote one fist on the desk before him. "William, in a big expedition like this, there are a lot of things that happen we can't always understand."

"What are you trying to say?"

"When we stopped over in Sitka, I received word from Colonel Charles Bulkley in charge of the expedition."

"About me?"

"Yes. You're not going ashore, William. You're to return to San Francisco aboard the *Golden Gate*. Colonel Bulkley wants you to take charge of the scientific operations during my absence."

CHAPTER FIVE

William didn't trust himself to speak. He fought back the tears of disappointment. Suddenly he thrust out his hand, "Good-by, Bob."

He waited until no one was watching, then he climbed aloft in the rigging, looking longingly at the rocky barren shore. He could see the activity on the beach where all the supplies had been landed. A few boats still crept from ship to shore. Down on the deck he could see Bob Kennicott shaking hands in farewell with Captain Scammon and the Mate. Kennicott climbed over the side and into the small boat that bobbed on the rolling waves. It pulled away, and gradually Bob's features became indistinguishable.

Then Captain Scammon gave a few quiet orders. Sailors at the windlass walked slowly about. The dripping hawser came inboard, dragging the anchor to rest in the bow. Others sprang aloft, looking curiously at William, and unfurled the sails. The masts leaned far over as the breeze took hold, and the bark was under way. Even as William watched, rain clouds rolled down and obscured the coast line. The land disappeared.

He was quite sure that he had seen the last of Russian America forever. He held tight to the rigging, fighting the waves of disappointment that washed over him. Then suddenly he shook his head, threw his shoulders back, and looked to the leaden sky. "I'm not a child," he whispered. "I'm a grown man. I've got work to do."

He clambered down the rigging, went to his cabin and busied himself labeling the specimens he had collected on Unimak Island. Gradually the hurt within him eased. There was a knock on the door, and Captain Scammon thrust his head in. "You'll be happy to know, Mr. Dall, I've got orders to spend the next six weeks over on the Siberian Peninsula, bringing supplies to the Western Union Telegraph Expedition. There will be a lot of opportunities for adding to your scientific collections."

The next day, on its course westward to Siberia, the *Golden Gate* passed St. Lawrence Island, long and low in the fog. Through the Captain's glass William looked at the dreary mass of black lava, dotted with volcanoes, without a single tree or shrub of any size on the entire island. As they drew closer he could see the island was covered with moss, lichens, grasses, creeping willows, stunted birches. The short beaches were crowded with driftwood.

"The islanders are great whale hunters," Captain Scammon said. "I've seen ten of them in an open boat kill a big bowhead whale with nothing but a hand-thrown harpoon. Most courageous act I've ever seen."

"Are we going ashore?" William asked eagerly.

Captain Scammon shook his head. "Sorry. We're going to be north in these waters too late as it is. I've spent two winters caught in the ice pack. Don't want to go through that again; not if I can help it."

The telegraph line was to cross between the North American and the Asiatic continents by means of a short submarine cable stretched under the narrow floor of Bering Strait. Then it was to drop overland in Siberia, cutting across the wide Gulf of Anadyr, again by submarine cable, before joining the long line of wires already rushing outward from European Russia.

From St. Petersburg to the Sea of Okhotsk stretched six thousand miles of forest, mountain, morass, and steppe, without roads and without bridges.

The *Golden Gate* had barely landed supplies at Plover Bay in Siberia, when a native came to the beaches with a note from American members of the expedition who asked for speedy aid. Captain Scammon immediately set out, and a week later returned with a half-dozen exhausted Americans.

"Couple cases of frostbite," he announced shortly. "Aside from that, it's mostly food these men need. They've been starving."

William tended to the men to the best of his ability. He frowned at the blackened toe of the bearded giant who loomed over him. "Guess you know my medical knowledge is slim," he confessed. "Captain heard I attended some medical lectures at Harvard—and that's why he made me Acting Surgeon."

"That's all right, son," the big man replied. "Just you look it up in the book, and do the best you can. I'm just all fired lucky to be alive."

Listening to the men, watching them wolf down enormous servings of food, William was able to piece together an incredible story of hardship.

"We been living with them tribes of Koryaks," the big man said between mouthfuls of food. "Natives, that is, like Indians. Tents is what they live in, even in winter like this—and follow the reindeer herds. The herds move, they move. That simple."

"Too simple," another grunted, gulping at a steaming cup of coffee. "We were bringing our telegraph line due north, and one day the Koryaks headed due east, and we were all alone. No wood. No shelter. Nothing. And all of a sudden it got so cold, I was afraid to snap my fingers, thinking they'd drop off."

"We'd like to have died," the big giant said simply. "This here beard became just like frozen iron wire, it was that cold."

"And my eyelids got so heavy with frost, couldn't keep my eyes open. Every time I winked, they froze together, and I had to pry 'em apart."

"It was the nights was bad," a thin voice said from the far end of the mess table. "Storming so bad the tents blew away. Couldn't build a fire."

"You must have had some shelter," William said.

"Piled the sledges together, if you call that shelter," the little man said. "We shoveled out the snow in the center, and tried building a fire on the open side. Wind blew it out. We just sat and froze and waited for that storm to blow out. Must have been there six weeks when we heard tell of an American ship coming down the peninsula. Guess if Captain Scammon hadn't come when he did, we'd just rolled over and died."

Listening to the tales of heroism from the survivors, William thought of Bob Kennicott and his men facing a winter of unknown terrors over on the other side of the Bering Strait. Despite the hardships and the close call from death that he saw written in the faces of the men huddled in the messroom, he still wished with all his heart he was back with Bob Kennicott and his band of brave men.

Slowly the *Golden Gate* crept down the length of the Kamchatka Peninsula in Siberia, making frequent stops to contact the different work parties who were surveying the two thousand miles of line that would traverse wild land.

At every opportunity William was ashore, alert for additions to his scientific collections. At night he busied himself in his tiny cabin with the jars and boxes which contained his treasures. The lamp overhead swung with the motions of the ship, and his shadow leaped from wall to wall. There were innumerable notes to be kept up, entries to be made in his journal, and detailed reports to be written to scientists who were waiting thousands of miles away for the news of the discoveries being made in the northland.

Bark GOLDEN GATE, *at sea*
November 14, 1865
Bound for San Francisco

To the Members of the Chicago Academy of Sciences.

Gentlemen:—A short account of the season's work, and the prospects for another season, may not be entirely devoid of interest for you.

The collections actually made amount to some 800 species, comprising about 10,000 specimens. Other collections, known to have been made but not yet come to hand, will add largely to this total.

I have taken charge of the scientific operations in Major Kennicott's absence, by his desire, and return to San Francisco.

The Expedition has visited Sitka, Ounga Island, Ounimak Pass, St. Paul Island, and St. Michael's; on the Asiatic side, Plover Bay, Anadyr Bay and Petropaulovski, the capital of Kamchatka; and obtained collections of great interest at all these places. Many interesting notes and drawings have also been made.

The prospect for next season is as bright as could possibly be desired.

I have the honor to be

Very respectfully yours,

WM. H. DALL

The little ship pushed far out into the rolling waters, making the long bend around the extreme tip of the Aleutian Islands, then setting course for San Francisco. The fogs that were so prevalent in the region rolled down with great regularity. One morning there was a dull booming, then there was the sound of footsteps running on the deck. William tumbled out to find all the sailors grouped along the port rail, trying to pierce through the thick sheet of fog rolling over the water. Even as they watched, a sheet of fire lit the horizon, a cannon ball screamed through the rigging, and there was the dull, thudding roar of sound.

"He's firing at us!" a sailor screamed. "It's a pirate! He's going to sink us!"

Out of the fog loomed a patch of white on white, and a trim schooner paralleled the course of the *Golden Gate*. William could see a little group of sailors in the bow. He could see the flame of a taper held ready. A megaphone was lifted and a deep voice came drifting across the intervening water, "Stand to or we'll sink you!"

Captain Scammon gave the necessary orders. Sailors leaped aloft, and the bark lost headway. Slowly the strange ship closed in. The group by the cannon stood ready, tapers flaring. William could feel his heart pounding with excitement. He looked at the mast of the strange ship, and there, drooping idly in the calm air, was the flag of the Confederacy!

64]

A young man wearing a deep blue pea jacket stood on the rail as the two ships closed. The cannon swiveled about until it pointed directly to the tight knot of sailors aboard the *Golden Gate*.

"Don't get any ideas," the young man called quietly. "We'll shoot at the slightest provocation." The two ships touched, and the young man leaped lightly aboard. "Who is in command?" he demanded.

Captain Scammon stood forward. "I am Captain Scammon. This is the bark *Golden Gate* of the Western Union Telegraph Expedition Fleet. We are citizens of the United States of America."

"And, I, sir, am Tonso McCrae, Captain in the Confederate Navy. You are my prisoners, sir. I will give you exactly ten minutes to lower your boat and pull away from your ship before I sink her. No one is to go below deck for any reason. Now make it lively, all of you."

"Captain McCrae!"

"You are wasting valuable time. Nine minutes."

"But, sir."

"Eight minutes, Captain Scammon. The responsibility for the life or death of your crew rests with you."

William could contain himself no longer. He walked determinedly forward to the young man who was scarcely his own age. "Captain McCrae," he said heatedly, "our Captain Scammon is simply trying to tell you that the war is over. Over, sir! We're no longer fighting! It's been six months since General Lee surrendered to Grant. Haven't you heard?"

Tonso McCrae whitened. He stepped forward.

"You're lying!"

William shook his head. "It's true. We sailed from San Francisco on May twenty-third—a full month after the surrender. In my cabin I have the San Francisco newspapers with the stories that came across the telegraph."

"Get the papers."

William ran. But already, his words had carried across to the Confederate vessel. He saw the tight groups leave the cannons and start to surge closer to the *Golden Gate*. He heard the words like a swelling chorus, "The war's over! We can go home! The war's over!"

He rushed to his cabin and scooped from under the bunk the six newspapers he had carried north. Then he ran back to Tonso McCrae, the newspapers flapping wildly in his hands. McCrae took them quickly without a word, his eyes going to the big black headlines. Then he turned to his crew.

"Men, it is true. The war is over. You've been granted amnesty. You're going home!"

A cheer went up from the seamen aboard the Confederate vessel.

William stood by Tonso McCrae's elbow. "Read the other papers, Captain McCrae. About President Lincoln."

McCrae looked at William curiously. Then he turned the papers. He stiffened when he saw the flaming headline, "LINCOLN ASSASSINATED!" He began to read the text closely, his eyes riveted to the black type. William could see the muscles of his jaws working. Slowly Tonso McCrae put the paper aside. He looked past William to the men of his ship. "President Lincoln has been assassinated," he announced slowly. "My brother is one of the group accused of the shooting. They think I'm implicated." He turned his head slowly, looking to the men of the *Shannon* and those of the *Golden Gate*. "There's a price of ten thousand dollars on my head," he said defiantly. "Anybody want to collect it?"

There was silence, all eyes fixed on the lonely figure who

stood by the rail. One of the Confederate seamen stepped forward.

"Captain, I've a wife and children I haven't seen for two and a half years. I want to go home to Alabama."

Another stepped forward. "I've been aboard the *Shannon* for thirteen months. We've sailed for 58,000 miles. I want to go back to my farm."

One after another the Confederate seamen spoke, and each time it was the same. They were tired of war. They wanted to go home and start life anew.

Tonso McCrae listened. Finally he nodded his head.

"All right. You're going home. But not in my ship. I'm not turning it over to any Yankee carpetbagger. Stay aboard here, all of you. I can sail my ship alone."

There was a moment of uneasy silence. Then the Confederate seamen started to drift away, disappearing below deck of the *Shannon*, reappearing with their few belongings, and clambering aboard the *Golden Gate*.

William watched intently. He saw the young captain standing alone as the last seaman climbed over the rail. He saw the proud, erect figure of young Tonso McCrae step back to the wheel. The two ships parted. A gust of wind came and gave life to the sails of the *Shannon*. It slipped away, and disappeared in the fog.

"Set sail," Captain Scammon called briefly. "We're heading for San Francisco."

But William remained in the stern, trying to pierce through the fog that surrounded them. Part of himself was out there in the fog, standing at the helm of the ghost ship, the *Shannon*.

For seven long months William felt as if he were a prisoner, chained to a desk in the expedition headquarters in San Francisco. So busy was he in the tumult of assembling ships and crews and personnel for the construction of the telegraph line that his scientific work suffered. He tried, at every free moment, to get out and explore the shore line south to Monterey Bay. He crossed the Golden Gate to wander along the rocky beaches that nestled beneath the headlands guarding the entrance to San Francisco Bay.

But it seemed as though his every waking moment was taken up in the recruiting and outfitting offices of the expedition.

The Western Union Telegraph Expedition was organized like an independent Army with one objective—the conquering of a wilderness. Engineer-in-chief was Colonel Charles S. Bulkley. Captain Charles M. Scammon was Chief-of-Marine, Major Robert Kennicott, Chief of the Scientific Corps; Scott R. Chappel, Quartermaster. Commissions were given to the various officers; flags and badges served to distinguish the different branches of service. William was assigned the rank of lieutenant though he rarely used the title.

Hundreds of hardy and daring men, most of them just returned from the Civil War battlefields, flocked to the outfitting point, ready for the first spring departure north in 1866. They were organized, uniformed, and disciplined in the Army manner, and were assigned to working divisions, Quartermaster's Corps, and Engineer Corps. Some were readied for work in the wilderness of Canada, working on the first section of the line from Portland north to Westminster, British Columbia. Exploration parties were pushed into the wilderness to hasten the erection of the line from Fort Fraser to Fort Saint James and through the lake region to Lake Takla, joining the Skeena River for the plunge down to the Pacific Ocean.

Others were detailed to the Siberian section, and still a third group, the one which William watched with greatest interest, to the basin of the Yukon River Valley where they would meet with Bob Kennicott and lead the telegraph line triumphantly across Russian America to meet with the Siberian section across the Bering Strait.

Twenty-two ships formed the life line that served the vast expedition spread across a large section of the world. William watched one ship after the other being outfitted with supplies, taking aboard the workmen, and slipping out past the Golden Gate, heading north into the Pacific. Each departure was a heartache, for he was sure the great adventure was escaping him.

Back at the office, he found a strange air of disquiet. "What's wrong?" William asked. "What's everyone so gloomy about?" For a moment he felt intense pain about his heart. "Any word from the Yukon as yet? Any word from Bob Kennicott?"

But his superiors shook their heads. "Not a word. We haven't heard anything from those people for eight months. But you can't expect any word—the Bering Sea is frozen solid. We wouldn't know if they're alive or dead—at least not until the telegraph line is pushed through."

"*IF,*" said another, emphasizing the word heavily. "Guess you know the second Atlantic cable is almost finished. If that's successful," the speaker made a motion as though he were slitting his throat Indian fashion, "that's the end of the Western Union Telegraph Expedition—it just won't be needed. It'll die a natural death in the wilderness."

"Rubbish," the first rejoined. "You and I saw the first Atlantic cable fail. It can't possibly survive thousands of feet down on the ocean floor. This telegraph line across Russian

America and through Siberia to the back door of Europe is the only way to get instantaneous communication around the world."

"I hope you're right—otherwise we're all going to be out of a job!"

All of May passed, and seven of the fleet's ships sailed northward. June passed, and ten others joined the parade of vessels busy ferrying supplies to every part of British Columbia, Russian America, and the long length of Siberia's Kamchatka Peninsula. Standing on Telegraph Hill, watching each ship in turn sail into the sunset beyond the Golden Gate, William was sure that the expedition would be completed, and he would never again sail north of San Francisco. He was heartsick and lonely, and several times he thought of resigning and returning to his native Boston. It was only the thought of Bob Kennicott, alone in the wilderness, perhaps waiting his return to Russian America, perhaps needing his help, that kept him faithful and unswerving.

Early in July, 1866, William received word he was to proceed north again. His hopes soared. Now he'd get to join Bob Kennicott. But even before the *Nightingale* sailed from the Golden Gate, his hopes were dashed. He was to remain with the little schooner while it made the supply run along Siberia's Kamchatka Peninsula. His particular scientific objective was to determine the exact height of the various volcanoes along the peninsula. It was to be interesting work—but William wanted with all his heart to join his friend in the Yukon.

On July 11, 1866, the schooner cleared the narrow opening of San Francisco Bay, and headed north and west for William's second voyage to the Arctic. Through mid-August and into September he performed his tasks with meticulous care, for he believed in rigid honesty in the work to be performed. Yet he chaffed during the interminable delays of the supply calls along the Expedition's ports on the Siberian Peninsula. He kept looking eastward over the Bering Sea, toward Russian America and Bob Kennicott.

On the night of September twenty-third, unable to sleep, William paced up and down with the officer of the deck. A driving storm from the northeast covered the deck with an inch of slippery, half-melted snow and hail. Looking over the side in the dim light, William could see the swelling waves of the Bering Sea yellow with sediment from nearby rivers.

"Tomorrow will see us in," the Mate said quietly. "That's mud from the Kwikhpak River you can see in the water."

The next morning the *Nightingale* crept through the rain and sleet, inching toward the low, rolling hills that framed Saint Michael's Island on the shores of Russian America.

A small boat pulled steadily toward them. William leaned far over to hail those in the little craft.

"Where's Kennicott?" he yelled through cupped hands.

There was no answer. Oars dipped, arms pulled, and the boat came closer to the *Nightingale*. Once more William leaned far over, straining, cupping his hands and calling, "Where's Kennicott? Bob Kennicott?"

A lone figure with long hair, beard, deerskin dress and hood stood erect in the stern. William recognized Fred Whymper, the naturalist, who had accompanied the leader. Whymper was silent, then his voice, low and clear, came across the waters.

"Kennicott is dead, poor fellow. Last May."

Dead! The young giant, nobly impetuous, aflame with the

fires that scientific knowledge ignites! William stepped back to hide his tears.

The small boat tied up alongside. Frederick Whymper came aboard to tell the story of the dead leader.

"We found out the Yukon and the Kwikhpak rivers were the same," he said quietly. "We started just after you people had left on the *Golden Gate* one year ago. We spent six weeks fighting upstream against the current, and found we had come less than fifty miles from the open ocean—the river bent and twisted so much. It took the heart out of Kennicott."

He went on in a tired voice. The first weeks of toil had been wasted, yet they continued their fight upstream, on their voyage of discovery along the muddy Yukon. Winter caught them at Nulato, two hundred miles up the great river. Kennicott was worn and discouraged. Several times messengers came overland from the seacoast, stumbling into the winter camp at Nulato with prodding notes from the office in San Francisco. The notes demanded querulously that Kennicott show more speed. They told of the tremendous strides being made across the Bering Strait in Siberia. They hinted that the crews in British Columbia would overtake the Yukon expedition before they had strung their first mile of wire.

Early in May the ice started to break loose on the river. The whole camp was fired with excitement. Kennicott was ready and eager for the year of exploration waiting.

Then, clutching his heart, he died.

William listened sadly as Whymper told how the men who had explored the wild country with him sewed the body of their leader in sealskins and went with it aboard a small canoe. They fought a constant stream of broken ice that surged about them, grinding and crushing. Whole trees and huge sections of bank were swept away in the funeral ride to the sea. When they came to Saint Michael's, they placed the body in a vault in the Russian fort, waiting for the coming of the *Nightingale*, when Bob Kennicott could be sent home.

When Fred Whymper finished telling the story of Kennicott's death, William left him abruptly, and returned to his cabin. He was afraid to trust his feelings before the strangely silent group crowded on the deck of the ship. He tried not to think of his dead friend who waited in the Russian fort.

CHAPTER SIX

Captain Scammon, master of the *Nightingale*, was the ranking officer of the Western Union Telegraph Expedition at Saint Michael's. He called William to his cabin.

"Dall," he said abruptly, "you know that the exploration here in Russian America had been divided into three sections." He jabbed his pipe at a map that swung above the chart table. "From the seacoast into Nulato, from Nulato up to Fort Yukon, and finally south to meet our people who are coming up from Canadian country. Ennis has everything under control here on the coast; we'll be ready to string wires before too long. Captain Ketchum is well acquainted with the country beyond Fort Yukon and he'll be in charge of that section. We need someone to be in charge of the stretch between Nulato and Fort Yukon—five, six hundred miles. Bob Kennicott's territory." He paused and exhaled a huge cloud of smoke. "I think you're the man."

William was unable to speak. He looked blankly at Captain Scammon. Finally he nodded. "Yes, sir. I'll try."

"Good." The Captain swung to his feet. "I've already notified Ketchum. He'll tell you all you need to know when you go ashore. Good luck, young man." He paused and looked critically at William. "How old are you?"

"Twenty-one."

Captain Scammon tried to hide the look of astonishment that passed over his tanned face. "Good luck," he repeated.

It was impossible to go ashore that night. A north wind raked the shallow water of the Sound. All through the night the schooner stirred uneasily. Tossing and turning in his bunk, William could feel the keel thumping hard into the muddy bottom.

In the morning the rains still fell, and the ground swells made travel ashore an impossibility. He waited until noon while a large scow was loaded with coal, then, sitting ignominiously on one of the larger lumps, he started the trip toward the low bluffs of Saint Michael's. The rain was cold and penetrating, and he shivered involuntarily. "How different," he thought, "from the arrival planned in the long nights back at San Francisco!" Suddenly he threw his shoulders back, and resolved to forget the rain, and the cold, and the discomfort. He was an explorer. He was defying the elements. He was a conqueror coming on a new land.

Out of the chill mist loomed a frail wharf, a temporary landing place that enabled the scow to pull close and unload. In winter the wood pilings were removed from the teeth of the sea ice that crushed everything within reach. Captain Ketchum was waiting on the wharf, his hand outstretched to aid William as the latter clambered upward.

"Not very dignified," William said as he clutched Ketchum's hand.

"Better arrival than mine," the Captain replied. "My first trip here I fell overboard. Took me two days to dry out. Come up to the fort and we'll discuss the plans for the winter."

William looked about as they trudged through the sand toward the low bluffs. The day was utterly dreary, bowed down with angry rain clouds. Back from the water were meadowlike flats, innumerable pools of water, the land gradually swelling to low hills in the background. A narrow channel, scarcely fifty feet wide, separated Saint Michael's from the mainland. The Russian fort was a collection of log buildings with plank roofs. A leaning flagpole conveyed the entire atmosphere of age and neglect. William was disappointed. Almost at once he wanted to get away, to start inland to the wilderness—to Bob Kennicott's wilderness.

He talked for hours with Captain Ketchum, going over the plans for the coming winter. Then, with some biscuits in his pockets to stave off his hunger, he rolled in his blankets on the hard wooden floor of a back room in the Russian fort. The rains poured down. Fine volcanic gravel seeped through the roof overhead. Dogs howled, and a bell tolled ominously. Far in a distant section of the fort he could hear the sounds of revelry from the Russian convicts who performed the work about the lonely outpost.

He stirred uneasily, then, utterly exhausted, fell asleep.

The days were spent in tremendous activity, getting ready the vast quantities of supplies brought by the *Nightingale* for transshipment northward along the coast to Unalakleet. It was at the latter village that the telegraph line would emerge from the Yukon wilderness, swing around the shore line of the Peninsula, then make the plunge under water to link with the copper wires being strung across Siberia.

The rain continued relentlessly, hampering the work of transferring the supplies to the smaller boats that could navigate the shallow waters north to Unalakleet. William scarcely had time to think of his scientific studies as he struggled with boxes and crates.

On the sixth night after his arrival he walked alone on the rocky beach that looked out upon Norton Sound. He felt the first winds of winter which were sweeping down from the Arctic. The sand beneath his feet was crusted and hardened, as though it were testing itself for the winter. Then it would be frozen solid and crushed beneath the ice waves that would pile up from the heaving sea.

He had been unable to sleep. Not only was he torn with grief for the death of his beloved friend, but the new responsibility frightened him. "God," he prayed, "give me the strength and the courage and the wisdom needed. Make of me a man like Bob Kennicott." Then he went back and curled in his blankets. But sleep still eluded him, and he rose to prowl the beaches again. In late September the nights were still short, and dawn came quickly. William looked overhead to the immense flocks of ducks starting the southward journey to the United States. The air was filled with darting movements of robins, rusty blackbirds, warblers, pine grosbeaks, and fox sparrows keeping busy in these last few hours before they flew south, escaping the fast rushing winter.

On the morning of October 1, 1866, he waited while Lieutenant Charles Pease escorted the body of Bob Kennicott out to the *Nightingale.* He stood in silence while the schooner turned to the west and disappeared over the horizon. The ship was their last link with the outer world. Soon the ice would come, and for seven months the Sound would be frozen solid, a barrier to all ships. There was a chance a dog team, carrying mail, would make the two hundred and seventy mile journey south to Nushagak on Bristol Bay. There was a chance, too, that a connection might be made with a ship sailing south to Sitka—but only a slim chance. To all practical purposes, the outer world disappeared with the sailing of the *Nightingale.*

For another week they labored without ceasing, assembling

equipment and supplies, sending material ahead by small boat to Unalakleet, sixty-five miles north on Norton Sound. There the working parties had started inland along the Unalakleet River, fighting across a portage that led through swamp and muskeg until the swift waters of the Yukon were encountered. Each night the temperature dropped to near zero; the wind blew with an eerie whistle, and ice pools formed in the tundra up from the beach.

The little coal steamers that had been sent north were found to be utterly useless in the strong currents of the Sound. They were hauled ignominiously out of the water, high on the beach. Their failure caused an even greater hardship for those who worked upon the beaches, preparing supplies for shipment to the inland bases.

William was beginning to find out what had been too often glossed over in the glowing accounts of men who blaze new trails in the wilderness—exploration entails a great deal of hard work.

One morning there was a loud "Halloo!" and he turned about to find a familiar figure trotting down the beach, carbine held high in greeting.

"Jonathan Benson!" he called.

"William! We got worried upriver at Nulato, waiting for you fellows. They sent me down to see if I could help things out."

"You've grown, Jonathan. A year's made a lot of changes in you."

"Yep. Two inches taller. Strong as an ox—and say, nobody's been hungry as long as I'm out with this gun. Bear, caribou, beaver—you name it; I'll shoot it!"

"Good. I'm glad you're staying with us for another year."

Jonathan looked about him. "I've learned a lot about this

country in a year, William. This beach is no place to be caught if things gets bad." He cradled the carbine in his arms as though it were alive. "You might wake up tomorrow and winter'll have this beach tighter'n a nut. If I were you, I'd take a chance and try to get moving to winter headquarters in Nulato."

William nodded his head in agreement. "That's exactly what we're going to do. The boats are ready. We'll leave in the morning."

Early on the morning of October eighth, William awoke to find the ground covered with snow. Out in the Sound were white cakes, miniature icebergs from the pack that had already formed far to the north. Captain Ketchum stood by his side, blowing vigorously on his hands. "We're getting started none too soon, William. Another week could see that Sound a solid sheet of ice."

William and Captain Ketchum started off in an oomiak—a large, open boat, flat bottomed and consisting of a wooden frame over which oiled sealskins were stretched. The wind was strong, biting cold. In eight hours they covered only twenty-two miles. They sought shelter in a native village, bedding down in the community bathhouse. The wind continued to blow with a steadily increasing force, racing with a high, screaming sound that seemed to be funneled directly downward from the North Pole. The bathhouse was warm, and the wind lulled William into an exhausted sleep. As he dropped off he thought to himself that never before had he worked so hard as in these days since landing on the beach at Saint Michael's.

The next morning the wind was still screaming across the Sound, whipping the water into a white foam. "At this rate,"

William said to Captain Ketchum, "it will take us all winter to get into Nulato."

"Patience, William, patience. The first trick in exploring is to keep alive—and warm, if you can."

But William's mind was in a continual torment. He kept thinking of the men who had gone ahead to Unalakleet, worrying for their safety. He kept thinking of the supplies still stacked in the open at Saint Michael's. He looked about the crowded bathhouse, and fretted at the lost time, the tasks still waiting.

"Captain Ketchum," he repeated, "we've got to get to Nulato. This storm has got to end."

Ketchum smiled, his firm red lips showing through the tangle of his beard. "Take it easy, William. Remember Kennicott. He worried the same way—and it killed him."

The next day the wind abated. The skin boats fought through the gathering shore ice toward Unalakleet. Several times during the long day the small flotilla of boats was almost swamped with sudden, vicious waves. When almost within sight of Unalakleet the fury of the equinoctial storm struck fiercer than ever. Exhausted with the continuous paddling, William had slipped beneath a deerskin blanket when suddenly there was a shout from Ketchum.

"Ice ahead!"

William sat upright. In the gathering darkness he could see large cakes of ice racing down on the flotilla, jagged menaces that could slash a hole in the skins with just a glancing blow. He leaned far over, shoving at the ice cakes, his hands and arms dipping into the bitterly cold water. For nearly an hour they fought their way shoreward, finally stumbling on the beach among the driftwood. They paused only long enough to haul the boats high from the reach of the water, then ran along the beach to the trading post. The noise of their coming, heralded by the barking of dogs, roused the sleeping inhabitants. They tumbled out and welcomed the freezing newcomers. After feeding them, the Russians insisted they take the beds which had been prepared.

William crawled in gratefully, utterly exhausted. He saw to his horror that the bedding was swarming with big black cockroaches. He shook his head regretfully, and, while he was still shaking it, he fell asleep.

The next morning, when it became evident that there would be another delay before the party would be able to start inland, William secured a tent, pitched it down by the beach, and moved his gear into it. "Even if I freeze," he told Ketchum, "I'm not going to sleep in that post again." He secured a long piece of driftwood, planted it as a flagpole, and lifted the ensign of the Scientific Corps into the strong breeze. Looking at it solemnly, he made the resolution to carry the blue cross and the scallop of the Scientific Corps where no other flag had yet floated in Russian America.

He was still shaking and shivering in the store clothes he had brought from San Francisco. It took only a few minutes and six dollars to obtain a dressed deerskin parka with a wolverine hood, and a pair of sturdy Eskimo boots made from the skin of reindeer's legs. For a few dollars more he purchased a bearskin to use as a bed, and an extra blanket of rabbitskins. Even when the tent was almost buried in snowdrifts, William remained warm and comfortable.

He could not restrain his impatience. Ketchum's experience enabled him to pass judgment on the inadvisability of continued traveling inland since the rivers were not yet frozen solid, but William chaffed at the delay. Ketchum did not try to hold him back when he decided to try to strike inland in company with an Eskimo guide. But the guide, after looking uneasily toward the northern sky, shook his head.

"I will not go," he said. "The storm will come again."

William fought back the rush of anger. "I've got to get started," he said quietly.

The Eskimo turned his back as though he had not heard, and walked away. "I'll cross alone," William decided. "I can't get lost. All I have to do is to follow the Winter Trail along the Unalakleet River, to the Kaltag portage, then. . . ." His voice trailed off, and suddenly he felt very foolish. He turned to Jonathan Benson. "You've been across, Jonathan. You can guide us."

The young hunter lifted his shoulders in a gesture of doubt. "That was before the freeze-up, before the snow fell. There were landmarks. A man could tell a bush from a rock—or a creek from dry land." He pointed to the dead-white waste of snow that followed the shallow valley on either side of the sluggish Unalakleet River. "What can you tell now?"

Reluctantly William agreed.

It was not until the twenty-fifth of October that Captain Ketchum was able to call, "We're leaving! Get the dog teams together! We'll make it this time!"

William started to trot down the trail, shuffling awkwardly on his unaccustomed snowshoes. They were soldiers fighting an invisible enemy, cut off from the rest of the Western Union Telegraph Expedition and from the entire world.

Besides William and Jonathan Benson there were Captain Ketchum, Lieutenant Michael Lebarge, both of them experienced explorers, and Mr. Francis, engineer of one of the small steamers used in unloading the supply boats.

There were four dog teams, the dogs at first curiously silent as if they, too, were reluctant to leave the shelter of the village and venture inland.

William was grateful for the experience of Ketchum who swung naturally into the lead. He found himself getting stiff and sore after only a few miles of traveling on snowshoes. He wondered, uneasily, if it would be he who would first fall.

That night, exhausted, he gathered with the others around the campfire, wolfing down biscuits and bacon, and sucking greedily on steaming cups of tea. He wrapped himself in blankets, looked for a few moments through the canopy of spruce branches, and fell into a sound sleep.

He woke with a start when Lieutenant Lebarge stepped on his shoulder.

"Excuse me, Mr. Dall," the Lieutenant said hastily. "Just got excited."

"What's wrong?"

"Some of the dogs didn't like our company. Chewed up their harnesses and hit the trail back to Unalakleet. Four of them."

Despite the loss of the dogs, the little party kept pushing inland, following the ice path of the frozen river.

In one of the odd quirks of the north, the weather suddenly turned warm. Instead of being welcome, it was greeted with groans by Ketchum and Lebarge. "Can't trust that river ice," they announced. "We'll wait."

"Hey, Captain!"

Mr. Francis came running up, an empty leather strap swinging in his hand. "Nine more dogs gone back to Unalakleet! We just can't keep them animals no how!"

A conference was held. William and Mr. Francis started on the trail toward Unalakleet to gather in the lost dogs. When they returned to the village by the frozen seas, they were greeted with hoots of derision. The dogs had already been sent back to Captain Ketchum, and their journey had been needless. William said nothing. He began to realize the heartbreaks and delays that had haunted Bob Kennicott to his death.

CHAPTER SEVEN

William never became accustomed to the interminable delays that hampered the expedition. It seemed to him that the fluctuating temperature became a personal enemy. For three weeks he was forced to remain in Unalakleet or the other native villages close by, with the weather alternately too warm for safe traveling on the ice of the rivers, or too cold for exposure outdoors.

The success of the expedition was always uppermost in his mind. Despite the vagaries of the weather, he joined in efforts to move the mountain of supplies slowly inland over the Kaltag portage, waiting for word from Ketchum, up ahead, to return to the forward party. He spent time with the natives, eager to learn as much of the Eskimo dialects as possible. He spent an equal time with the Russian workmen and convicts in an effort to learn the rudiments of their language. He kept his pencil moving constantly as he compiled notes for the book he intended to write upon his return to civilization. He struck out boldly into the wilderness, alone, eyes and ears alert to the little things that would tell him the story of this vast white country that brooded in silence during the early winter.

One noon he started out despite the strong northeast wind that was blowing and the sharp blasts of fine snow. He stuffed his pockets with biscuits, walked out on the smooth ice of the river and was nearly blown to the surface by the violence of the wind. He was determined to rejoin Ketchum and make the dash to the winter quarters upriver at Nulato. The sleet was so blinding that he was unable to face into it, and proceeded at a half-crouch, crawling forward laboriously.

Hour after hour he clawed his way forward. He realized the foolishness of his venture, yet was too frightened to turn about for fear the trail had been covered. The gloomy afternoon became night with terrifying suddenness. William was forced to grope his way over ice hummocks and snowdrifts, fighting his way into the wind and sleet. Suddenly the ice gave way beneath him. He threw himself far to one side in a wrenching motion. He was wet to the knees. He huddled in the shelter of an undercut bank, pulled off his boots and socks and wrung the water out of them. When he replaced his socks and boots they froze stiff. He remembered the stories of men who had become wet, and lost their toes and feet from freezing.

H thought uncertainly of starting a fire with which to dry himself, but a sudden chorus of wolf howls made him decide against the move. He had to find shelter.

He pushed ahead doggedly, and finally saw, in the light of the new moon that was shoving high above the alder trees, a snow-banked cabin. He hurried forward, pounded on the door and was admitted by a wide-eyed native. The Indian produced a long-handled knife. William backed away, but the Indian knelt before him, cut the laces and proceeded to pull off the stiffly frozen boots. He pointed to the fire, grinning.

After a three-week separation William finally rejoined Captain Ketchum who was still marooned at the halfway mark to the winter headquarters at Nulato. As soon as William greeted his friends, Ketchum gave the signal to get underway again. The dogs barked and leaped forward; the heavily loaded sleds skidded, and slid, and straightened. The explorers passed over hillsides sparsely wooded with spruce and alder. They went through valleys, climbed over hills, and broke out into the open tundra.

William could feel himself growing stronger. He gloried in the endless physical effort that was demanded in the conquering of this northland. He lifted the hood of his parka and felt the strong north wind blowing full in his face. The wind hurled the snow forward in a blinding sleet. He knew the temperature was well below zero. Yet he was never so happy. He was moving forward into the wilderness.

They camped that night in a thicket of alder, placing the sleds to windward with a piece of cotton drill stretching around them, helping to ward off the driving snow. The cup of hot tea burned William's hand on one side while the wind gnawed it on the other. The dogs curled in balls, gradually disappearing under the snowdrifts. William shivered in his blankets, looking at the red eyes of the wind-driven fire, and tried to sleep.

No matter how great his exertions or overwhelming his discomforts, he still found time to add to his collections destined for the Smithsonian Institution.

Finally he had his first glimpse of the mighty inland river which he hoped to explore in the coming spring. Ketchum had spoken to him as they neared the spot, and William, in a typical burst of enthusiasm, had rushed ahead, clambering over the flanks of some high hills. He felt like another explorer, Balboa, who had rushed forward into the Pacific. William slipped down the snow-clad hill, forgetting everything else in his desire to be the first on the broad, smooth ice of the Yukon.

From his vantage point he could see a forty mile expanse of the river east and west of the point where the winter trail touched it. It was snow-covered, with broken fragments of ice cakes glowing in the ruddy light of the setting sun. It was three miles wide at the point where he stood, the opposite shore a faint black streak on the horizon. He was enthralled at the serpentine twisting of the frozen river, a gleaming white sheen almost lost in the dead-white expanse of snow. Only the close hugging thickets and the high bluffs on either side betrayed the true nature of the frozen highway that stretched far down to the Bering Sea.

William's heart pounded with exertion and excitement. This was the river of which he had read and dreamed. He was glad that he stood alone, for he did not wish the others in the party to know of his emotion.

They were still thirty-six miles from the safety of the fort at Nulato. The temperature was sagging ominously. At first they decided to push forward, but Ketchum's experienced judgment soon called for a halt. When the short hours of daylight were ended, the weary travelers turned to the left bank of the river, seeking a broad ravine. Lacking other shelter, they scooped deep holes in the snow, then men and dogs crept downward, huddling together for warmth.

William was the last man in. He lowered himself into the tight group of packed bodies, grateful for the slow warmth that was beginning to touch them. "God keep us safe," he prayed, then fell into an exhausted sleep.

In the morning they crawled from their shelter, harnessed the dogs and pressed forward. Each of the four sleds, loaded with nearly a ton of supplies, was pulled by seven dogs spread fanwise. The gray, shaggy-coated lead dog on the forward sled was a female, soon to bear a litter of pups. Watching her padding tirelessly forward, mile after mile, William marveled at her stamina. Jonathan nodded when he saw William's interest. "That's another reason we've got to get to Nulato. Sawashka is going to have a litter any day. If she has her pups out on the trail, every one of them will die."

The explorers pushed out on the river, the bluffs on either side seeming to squeeze inward, tossing the ice cakes high, and making travel difficult.

At midday William fed the dogs. He stood by the lead dog, reaching out to stroke the thick fur as he had done so often during the journey. But for once the dog growled at him menacingly.

"What's wrong, Sawashka?"

The dog continued the deep throaty growling, teeth bared as though ready to bite. William retreated. When he gave the word to go forward, Sawashka was missing. She had chewed through the rawhide tug line, and bounded into the wilderness.

Far ahead the stockade and the two turrets of the fort loomed on the left bank of the river. The brigade pressed forward. William and Jonathan raced up the bank. Dogs started an unearthly howling. Other members of the expedition who had gone before hurried out at the noise and shouted words of greeting.

William was anxious to inspect the fort where he would spend the next six months waiting for the ice to go out before deeper penetration into the Yukon Valley could be attempted. He looked with a great deal of curiosity at the slender trees that formed the walls of the stockade. The stockade had been built less than fifteen years before because of one of the most terrifying massacres in the north. William remembered his father recounting in shocked tones the grisly tale that had somehow seeped far to the south and east to Boston. A handful of Russian traders had been living here in comparative peace with the Indians who had tolerated their intrusion. In the spring of 1851, Lieutenant Barnard of the British Navy had come in search of some missing English explorers. Unwittingly he had insulted the Indian chief, and the insult had led to the massacre of more than one hundred Indians who lived close to the fort, of all the Russians, and of Lieutenant Barnard. Afterwards the stockade had been erected. William knew, from the stories he had been told by Captain Ketchum, that many of the Indians who had participated in the bloodletting still lived and traded at the post.

Within the fort were two large log buildings and a smaller one that had been designated for the use of the Americans. William reached up and touched the low ceiling. He paced twenty feet one way, and ten feet the other. He shrugged his shoulders. "It's small, but we should be able to keep warm."

"Take another look," Jonathan said, "I spent last winter here, and I know. Like to froze to death." He pointed to the gut which served as a window, and to the wide cracks in the flooring.

"Can't do much about the window," William observed. "Haven't seen a piece of glass since we left Saint Michael's. But this floor will have to be fixed."

"You fix it, William," Captain Ketchum commented, "and we'll get you a medal. Been losing all our needles, forks, and spoons down them cracks. Get out your thermometer and see how cold it is on the floor."

But William was already busy stuffing moss into the cracks. When the moss disappeared, he stuffed straw into the yawning holes. Finally, in desperation he covered the entire flooring with a thick bedding of straw, piled on mats, then nailed over the assemblage a half dozen old blankets. Captain Ketchum chuckled when he saw the result. He dug into the corner and tossed some reindeer skins into the center of the room.

"Rugs," he announced. "All the comforts of home."

Ivan Pavloff, the commander of the trading post, had already presented himself. The bearded Russian kept peering about the small room. When he left there was an undeniable look of disappointment on his face.

"What's wrong with him?" William demanded.

"He couldn't find your alcohol," Fred Whymper explained. "As soon as he does, it will disappear. He drinks it like water. If I were you I'd poison all the alcohol you use for your specimens and make sure old Ivan hears about it."

William was shown the spot on the frozen riverbank where Bob Kennicott had slumped forward and died. "We'll take up where he left off. We'll get that line of poles down to the Bering Sea."

That night when he returned to the cabin with Fred Whymper and Jonathan, he heard an odd noise. He looked inquiringly at Whymper. "Rats?"

"Don't think so. Didn't see any last winter. Just too darn cold for them. I've seen lots of mice, though." He looked sideways at William, grinning slightly, "*Microtus operarius endaecus*, if you want it straight from the book."

"I don't want mice in any form," William retorted. "I'm going outside and take a look."

He went down on his hands and knees and peered under the cabin. He struck a match, and looked long and carefully. Then he hurried back inside. "You're part right, Fred. Sawashka's had her pups. We got husky dogs for company!"

The days were extremely short, yet William tried to use every minute of the hours when the sun lifted in the leaden skies before wheeling and dropping beneath the dim horizon. He continued to add to his collections. He set traps for foxes and other small animals, not for their furs as the Indians did, but in order to obtain their skeletons to add to his boxes of specimens. Kurilla, the Indian who served as the cook for the Americans, also was an excellent shot. He went out with William almost daily, his rifle bringing down an assortment of birds that were eventually to appear in the display cases of the Smithsonian Institution.

William sketched the various scenes about Nulato with great intentness if not skill. In addition he continued his study of the Russian language and the various dialects of the Indian tribes who lived near the fort.

In the long evenings when the explorers were seated about the stove in the cabin, the group discussed plans for the coming season. Captain Ketchum and Lieutenant Lebarge would journey over the ice toward Fort Yukon, and already they were busy constructing the sleds to be used. Mr. Dyer was scheduled to descend the river and explore the unknown delta. William, accompanied by Jonathan Benson and Fred Whymper would fight upstream along the Yukon nearly six hundred miles to Fort Yukon. But their journey would be delayed until the ice had gone out late in May.

One of the main endeavors of the long winter was the erection of Fort Kennicott, to the south of Nulato, a log building which would be the permanent headquarters of the Western Union Telegraph Expedition in the Yukon Valley.

As the weeks sped by, and the bitter weather hampered the preparations for the coming exploration, William become more and more worried. He paced restlessly in the stockade on the banks high above the river.

That night Fred Whymper spoke to him. "William, I spent a year watching Bob Kennicott. I've spent two months watching you." He shook his head seriously. "You've got to slow down." He faced William across the table, speaking earnestly. "Why don't you go away for a spell? There's nothing more you can do here. The work will be accomplished, and we'll be ready for the spring."

"Nothing I'd like better than a chance for exploration— even now, in the dead of winter. But I can't go."

"You can, and you will." Whymper rose to his feet determinedly. "This place will still be here when you get back. Take Sawashka for company. I'll have Jonathan fix you some supplies."

Reluctantly William agreed. He had a great yearning to be close to the sea, even though, at this time of the year, it would be a solid sheet of ice. When he left Nulato he turned westward along the Nulato River, hoping to break through to meet an unnamed river beyond the range of barrier mountains that would lead down to Norton Bay. Sawashka trotted by his side, carrying supplies in two packs slung on her back. William carried a Sharps carbine.

The days were extremely short. When the sun broke through the dim haze it was close to ten o'clock in the morning. By two o'clock it had disappeared.

At every waking moment he was alert to almost unnoticeable signs of life about him. He kept scientific notes on the growth of the spruce and birch and the dwarf willow lining the riverbanks. Even when he was chopping firewood, or stripping birch bark for kindling, his mind was active. The mosses and lichens on the sheltered side of rocks and trees had a scientific message for him. He noted the wolves, foxes, snowshoe rabbits, lemmings, weasels, and field mice that still moved about in the darkness of winter. His eyes were alert for the movements of ptarmigans, owls, and ravens.

On the downward slope toward the frozen waters of Norton Bay he became lost. He continued westward into the sun, knowing that inevitably he must come to the sea. By accident he broke his sunglasses, and even though the sky was dark and overcast, the diffused light still caused snow blindness. His eyes burned and stung. Ripping off a piece of bark, he slit holes in it, and bound it across his eyes. But the pain was still intense. He knew that he must bind his eyes and remain in complete darkness for several days. And that was an impossibility.

Fighting the pain that never gave him a moment's peace, he staggered down the rough, hummocky slope that led to the sea, his eyes almost shut, groping his way. When the pain became so intense he could no longer bear it, he bandaged his eyes, held tight to the leather thong about Sawashka's neck, and walked in the darkness.

His supplies were exhausted. He was growing weak from hunger. Yet the pain in his snow-blinded eyes was paramount.

Blinded, shivering with the ceaseless pain that stabbed through his eyes, he stumbled against a hut high on the beach. He pulled himself hand over hand along the tilted side, felt his way inside a door, and tumbled into one of the bunks. He heard the dog sniffing by his side, then the padding of feet, and he was alone.

For twenty-four hours he remained motionless in the bunk, neither asleep nor awake. He had wrapped a thick scarf about his eyes, and gradually the pain subsided. But vision was slow to return. He huddled under the skins on the bunk, opening one eye cautiously, then the other, trying to pierce through the misty curtain. The pain returned with the slightest light, and he kept his eyes closed.

On the second day he pulled himself from the bunk and fumbled about the hut. It had an oddly familiar touch, and an incongruous air, as though it were entirely foreign to the wind-swept beaches facing Norton Sound. But it gave adequate shelter, and he asked no more.

He touched a stove by one wall, a box of kindling, but there was no food, and after his initial excitement at finding shelter, his strength failed him. He was unable to crawl beyond the door for the necessary driftwood. After the second day the fire guttered and went out. He returned to the bunk and covered himself with skins.

Almost as if in a dream he heard the door swinging back, and the sound of footsteps entering the small hut. He turned his head, but he was unable to pry open his eyelids. "My name," he said in a whisper to the newcomer, "is William Healey Dall, scientific director of the Western Union Telegraph Expedition. May I ask—who are you?"

"We've met before," the stranger replied, walking closer to the bunk. "My name is Tonso McCrae, and this is the cabin of my ship, the *Shannon*."

CHAPTER EIGHT

"I ran the *Shannon* on the beach," Tonso explained as he busied himself at the stove. "I knew I couldn't go on sailing her forever. And I figured as long as this country belongs to Russia, I could just as well hide out here as anyplace." He ducked outside and returned with a frozen quarter of caribou that he hung by the stove to thaw. "First good storm last winter knocked the masts out and lifted the ship high on the rocks. I salvaged what I could. I've been able to kill enough game to keep going. Only thing," he added almost wistfully, "gets lonesome here. Mighty lonesome."

William sniffed appreciably at the delightful odors drifting from the stove. He pulled himself upright eagerly when Tonso approached with a bowl of soup. "No sense in you living alone," William said between mouthfuls. "Why not join the expedition? We can use a man with your talents."

"Are you going to explore or fight a war?" Tonso asked incredulously. "What good would a sailor be to you?"

"After the ice goes out we'll be on the water ninety per cent of the time," William retorted. "We won't be fighting a war against people, but against time. We've got only five months to explore a wilderness."

"I'll think it over," Tonso replied, noncommittally. "For a little while you're not going anywhere. You're too weak to crawl out the door. Have some more soup. Got a strange dog been hanging around I've got to feed."

"Sawashka!" William exclaimed. "It must be Sawashka. She led me here."

"In that case, I'll give her doubles. Isn't often I get company."

For another week William lay stretched out on the bunk while the bandage remained on his eyes. Finally the pain disappeared. With the food that Tonso forced on him, his strength came back rapidly. He removed the bandage and for the first time saw McCrae clearly. The young sea captain had a full shaggy beard that made him appear much older than he actually was.

"You look like General Lee," William commented.

"And you're not too far off from Abe Lincoln with that set of whiskers yourself." Tonso stroked his beard proudly. "I'm not shaving this off until spring. Best wind breaker a man ever had. And even then I'll think twice about it. You don't know how bad the mosquitoes are up in this country once the water is free. Terrible."

William nodded thoughtfully. "I know. Several of the men quit and went back on the *Nightingale* because of them. Drove them almost mad." He walked unsteadily to the door and looked over the expanse of snow on the beach, and over the jumbled heaps of ice where the frozen breakers met the shore. "I must get back to Nulato. I've been gone three weeks. They'll be worried."

"I'll get you back," Tonso promised. "But not for another week. You couldn't last five miles on the trail."

Every day the two young men sat about the roaring fire, listening to the wind that raced down from the Arctic. When the wind was silent the cold became alive, causing the timbers in the ship's cabin to creak and groan. Tonso spoke of his youth on a plantation in South Carolina, of his parents, and his brothers, dead in the war or hunted as criminals. His anger was deep and intense. Listening to him, William felt a wave of helplessness. There was nothing he could do save talk of science, and the miracles of science, and the fascination of the tiny things of the sea that lived and multiplied while men fought and killed each other. Sometimes, looking at Tonso who stared so intently at the red glowing stove, he doubted if the other was listening.

"Someday," William said, "when the Expedition has finished its scientific work, I'd like to stay here in Russian America. I want to trace the northern timber line. I'd like to make a catalog of all the animals and birds north of the Arctic Circle. Most of all I'd like to obtain specimens of all the crustaceans. I wish. . . ." He looked sideways and saw Tonso was not listening. Shaking his head, he stood and placed his arm around his friend's shoulder. "Forget the war, Tonso. It's finished."

But McCrae was silent. The pupils of his eyes narrowed, reflecting the pin point of red light flashing back from the stove.

William walked to the door and stepped outside. There was a shadow moving in the darkness that came close and rested by his feet. He leaned down and patted Sawashka.

Suddenly he heard a thin, crackling noise. The dark blue of the sky became inflamed with colored, flashing signals. He watched as long weaving fingers of light, hissing and spluttering, snaked across the vaulted heavens. "The aurora borealis," William whispered to himself. It seemed as though invisible hands were sweeping across the night sky, dragging banners of light behind. The light came in a steady glow, then in electric flashes like the forerunner of a fierce storm. He saw that they were white, then blue, then tinged with red. The color came like the sweep of water over Niagara Falls, then in staccato fashion, almost like an artillery barrage.

"Tonso!" William called, "Come quickly!"

Tonso McCrae stood framed in the light of the candle that brightened the interior of the cabin. He lifted his face to the sky, watching the play of mysterious colors, flickering and faltering above the Bering Sea. The inner rings of light were more intense in some parts of the rings than in others. They advanced in ripples, compressed by the wind. From the brighter portions of the rings light streams of color dripped downward.

Looking at Tonso, William saw the glint of tears in his eyes. He pretended not to notice.

"I'll get wood for the fire," he said quietly.

He walked back from the beach, the dog shaking herself and following him. Overhead the aurora borealis spread and enlarged, the light becoming fainter. Suddenly, as though a broom had wiped across the sky, the colors disappeared. They came back for a moment, flared brightly, then dimmed away. Overhead the moon was a bright white disk, tinged blue with the intense cold.

From the bottom of a frozen creek twigs of the creeping willow thrust upright through the crusted snow. William kicked the snow away, plunging deeper into the drift until he was able to swing the short ax at the roots of the willow. He ripped and tore at the gnarled branches, piling them higher and higher on the snow outside the hole he was digging.

Finally he dragged the mound of roots and branches back to the cabin. He found Tonso stretched in the bunk, staring moodily at the low ceiling. He said nothing when William dragged the wood inside the cabin and piled it within easy distance. William rammed the stove full of wood. The cold was trying to creep within the cabin. The white rim of hoarfrost between the planks, always an indication of the falling temperature, deepened and widened.

"Thank heavens for shelter," William said, trying desperately to make conversation with the moody Tonso. "Hope the men at Nulato are as well protected."

Tonso rose from his bunk and thrust more wood on the fire. The flame from the candle flickered, cast big shadows on the far wall. "I followed the coast line down south below Cape Denbigh, last fall. There's an Eskimo village there, and a Russian trader." He looked into the flames. "He told me about a rumor that the United States is going to buy Russian America."

"We couldn't be that lucky! Buy all this immense country! Why, it's twice the size of all of Texas."

Tonso McCrae didn't hear. "If that's true," he said, as though William had not spoken, "there will be no safety for me here. It means I've got to run again. I'll be running the rest of my life."

At that moment a frigid blast roared across the open sea and hit in full fury. The door blew open, and Tonso sprang to throw his weight against it, forcing it closed. The wind shot down the funnel of the stovepipe, knocking it into two pieces. Smoke and ashes and soot flew through the air. The door of the stove burst open under the sudden pressure, and hot embers shot out across the earthern floor. William leaped to his feet, jumping in every direction as he tried to repair the damage.

Tonso stood with his back against the door, holding down the fierce pressure of the wind. He threw his head back and laughed uproariously. "That's what I get for feeling sorry for myself," he said between choking spurts of laughter. "We better figure on keeping alive tonight, rather than what's going to happen years from now!"

Outside the door Sawashka lifted her nose to the sky and her long, quavering challenge to the wind was wafted aloft. William and Tonso exchanged glances. Without another word, Tonso opened the door a few inches and called to Sawashka. The dog slipped inside, shook herself vigorously, and curled up in a corner.

Tonso blew out the candle and crawled into his bunk. "Tomorrow," he said, "we'll start back to Nulato. If you still want me in your expedition, I'm your man."

The stove glowed red and white, and gave out small sounds as it fought the wind. The dog stirred uneasily in the corner. William listened, and then fell asleep.

A few days later, William Healey Dall and Captain Tonso McCrae rejoined the expedition at the fort in Nulato. Jonathan Benson was particularly overjoyed to see William. "We were plenty worried. I wanted to start out looking for you— but Fred Whymper, he said just be patient, you'd show up, and by golly, you did! Look at the moose I shot last week!"

The members of the expedition looked curiously at Tonso McCrae. There were some who whispered against him, and the word "renegade" was used freely. But Tonso kept his temper. His jaw tightened. He plunged vigorously into the tasks that William had outlined for him.

Ivan Pavloff, the commander of the trading post, came each day to the expedition cabins. Half-Russian, he had learned the rudiments of English, and maintained a garbled liaison between the two groups. His son Peetka, eight years old, tagged along, keping well in the background.

One cold morning Jonathan ran to William's cabin and threw open the door. "Little Peetka shot his fingers off with a musket. We've got to do something! Those Indians, they're just standing around waiting for him to bleed to death."

William reached hastily for the few medical supplies that were stored in his cabin. Before he could get started, Tonso McCrae had bounded past him and was running along the worn, icy path that led to the Indian village. By the time William reached the village he found Tonso already kneeling by the screaming boy, bathing the three torn stumps of fingers on the left hand. The stolid-faced Indians stood in the background, moving only when Tonso requested warm water and clean bandages.

William knelt by his side. One glance showed him that the use of the fingers was gone forever. "We'll clean them thoroughly," he said. "Sew them up. Just hope there's no infection."

Tonso nodded. "Ive seen sailors aboard my ship die with less of a wound than this. It was the gunpowder, smoke, and dirt that killed them. Gangrene."

"You think my son die?" Ivan Pavloff asked.

"Not if we can help it," Tonso replied vigorously. "Tell him we're going to take care of him. Tell him it's going to hurt. That he must be brave."

The father spoke a few words; the boy lying on the pallet of skins stopped crying and nodded, his big brown eyes luminous with fright. Tonso cleaned the wound thoroughly, then sewed it with thread and needle. He looked around at the dirt and disorder that was common to the Russian cabins. He spoke to Ivan.

"It will be better if we take the boy back to our cabin and care for him there until he is better."

The father nodded. Tonso swept the boy up into his arms. As he walked down the trail with his frail burden, William said dryly: "If little Peetka survives, we're heroes. If he dies, we may as well move camp. There've been massacres up and down this river, and we'd be likely candidates for murder."

"This boy's going to live," Tonso replied grimly. "I promise you."

Young Peetka, under Tonso's vigilant care, rallied from his ordeal, and was soon on his feet. From that day on he tagged after Tonso McCrae. He went out on the trail and showed him how to snare snowshoe rabbits. He plunged into the thickets of dwarf spruce, and led him to the spots where ptarmigan were eager to answer a secret call.

One day he brought in a marten. "For my fingers," he said.

Young Jonathan Benson, nursing his carbine on his knees, was disgruntled. "That Tonso McCrae, he got himself a built-in guide. Me, I got to go out and work hard to find a little duck or goose that forgot to fly south. I can't even see snowshoe rabbits, let alone shoot 'em. Why," he said in an aggrieved voice, "if this keeps up, you won't even need a hunter to feed you people. That little Peetka will just have you all chomping on snowshoe rabbits Monday through Sunday."

"Never mind, Jonathan," William said. "Takes a lot of rabbits to keep this expedition going. You scare us up a moose. Soon we'll be taking off for the Interior, and we're depending on you to keep us from going hungry."

William added to his endless activities by taking measurements for a chart of the Yukon River. He busied himself with the instruments necessary for taking meteorological observations, and he remained always faithful to the collecting of natural history specimens. Going out with either Peetka or

Kurilla for an hour daily, he kept adding to his treasures—redpolls, downy and three-toed woodpeckers, pine grosbeaks, titmice, hawk owls, and bullfinch. The Indian children about the fort aided his searching. Armed with bows and arrows they scanned stumps and crevices looking for field mice. When successful they ran with their prizes to William, sure of a few beads or some trinket to repay them for their labor. On long dog-sled travels with their parents they still remembered to snare birds and mice, and to guard them carefully until their return to the fort. Some of their findings William considered of great scientific value.

All the expedition members brought him likely specimens that could be added to the swelling number awaiting shipment back to the Smithsonian Institution. Before the long winter was finished he had filled two large boxes with specimens of natural history and prepared them for the long journey back to the seacoast and far south to the States.

There were days of uncertainty, days when the weather became so warm that the snow adhered in large lumps to the snowshoes of those out on the trail. Even a short distance on the trail in those circumstances was exhausting. On the heels of the warm weather would come a spell of bitter temperatures—still, silent days when the mercury in thermometers would sag out of sight. To be caught on the trail in those days, without adequate shelter, was an invitation to quick death from freezing. Worst of all were the infrequent wind storms that raced through the river valleys, slashing at the unwary traveler as though resenting anyone who dared to be abroad in the hours when the wind was a tyrant.

In spite of the inconsistencies of the weather, Captain Ketchum and Lieutenant Lebarge were impatient to start on their six hundred mile journey to Fort Yukon. William was reluctant to see them leave. "You don't have enough provisions," he cautioned. "You're not sure of getting enough game to keep you alive."

Captain Ketchum agreed. "That's true. But we've still got to get started. I must be at Fort Yukon before the ice goes out if we're going to make contact with our people coming up from Canadian territory."

Even the Indians who had promised to accompany Ketchum and Lebarge refused to leave. Ivan Pavloff raged at the Indians. "You are cowards," he spat at them, "not willing to trust your lives where even a child would go." He looked at Captain Ketchum. "My son, Peetka, will accompany you. In no other way can I show my faith that you are strong and brave men."

"Couldn't have a better man along than young Peetka," Captain Ketchum agreed. "He'll keep us alive when everything else fails."

Jonathan Benson, listening, made a face. "Gosh," he muttered, "I'm sixteen years old. Guess I'm just too old to be of any use to this expedition any more."

"Cheer up, Jonathan," William smiled. "Two months from now, when it's our turn to start upriver, we'll have that gun of yours red-hot keeping us in food."

Yet he was uneasy when he stood in the falling snow and watched Ketchum and Lebarge call to the dogs, lean against the heavily laden sleds, and start moving slowly away. If their guns did not supply them with sufficient game to feed the dogs and party, they faced certain starvation.

"Hoist the flag," he said quietly to Jonathan. "They'll want to look back before they make the bend in the river."

Jonathan ran the Stars and Stripes high into the still air, then lifting his carbine, he fired a volley in farewell to the explorers who were fading in the gathering gloom.

Early in April, William found a willow catkin pushing above the snow. He chanced on a white-winged crossbill, and pounced eagerly on the steel-green musk beetles emerging from their burrows on the sod roof of the trading post.

One of the Indians was preparing to return to Unalakleet on the coast. Because it would be the last chance in months to send out letters, William hurriedly drew up his report to the expedition headquarters in San Francisco, detailing progress to date and telling of the departure of Ketchum and Lebarge. He also sent his customary letters to his friends in the Academy of Sciences at San Francisco and at Chicago. A detailed account of his scientific activities he addressed to the Smithsonian Institution in Washington. He wrote to his mother in Boston, and to his father in India he spoke of the coming of spring in the Yukon Valley.

"It's coming on with eager steps. The great snow blanket six or eight feet deep sinks and hardens each day. A tremulous mist hovers over the brilliant surface."

The white ptarmigan in the area began to molt, brown feathers appearing, sure signs of the coming spring. William glanced upward. Overhead the skies were beginning to fill with birds returning for the summer. Hawks and owls were nesting, and the screams of the young jays were already harsh in the air. He listened as the first geese honked through the air, heading northward. The first white swans drifted majestically to a landing in the shallow lagoons surrounding the river.

On the thirteenth of May, the anniversary of Robert Kennicott's death, William erected a cross on the banks of the river where his friend had died. On it was a tablet with the words:

IN MEMORY OF
ROBERT KENNICOTT
Naturalist
who died near this place
May 13, 1866, aged thirty

They had readied a skin boat for the journey. William made sure all was in order. The night before the departure he called the small group about him.

"We've received no word from Captain Ketchum and Lieutenant Lebarge," he said, "but that's to be expected."

In that sparsely settled country, where no more than a handful of white Russian traders were isolated in tiny trading posts, men were literally swallowed by space. The river basin was a vast valley of silence that swept through a deserted land.

"The first task of this expedition," he said slowly, "is to determine if it will be possible to use the Yukon Basin as a route for the telegraph lines that are pushing up from British Columbia. Our second task is to add as much scientific knowledge as possible to what little we know of Russian America. The Western Union Company is convinced that immigrants will follow the telegraph lines, just as they followed the railroad lines down in the States. We want to be ready to answer the questions that they will ask. What's this country like? What are the resources? Timber, coal, other minerals? Can the land support farm animals and crops? How warm does it get in the summer? How cold does it get in the winter?"

"Gosh, William," Jonathan interrupted, "I know a lot of the answers. Whyn't you just ask me?"

"What was the highest temperature recorded last August at Nulato?"

"Well," Jonathan replied, hesitating, "I remember I was perspiring."

"That isn't exactly a scientific answer, Jonathan."

"You're right, William," the boy agreed. "What we need are more thermometers!"

"More of everything in the line of scientific instruments, Jonathan—and we'll have them."

On the fifteenth of May, 1867, the river ice heaved, pushed upward by a tremendous force. It cracked in long, jagged splinters and started to rumble and roar as it inched down toward the sea. Jonathan came running to William. "She's going out!" he yelled. "The ice is going out! Hip! Hip! Hooray! Hooray for the river!"

William was caught up in the wave of enthusiasm. Even the Indians moved about with alacrity, looking always to the rumbling river. He ordered a final examination of the boats that would carry them upstream. There was something he had to tell Jonathan. Remembering his own disappointment when he was first denied a chance to go ashore at Saint Michael's, he spoke with reluctance to the eager young boy who stood before him.

"The expedition will split in two parts, Jonathan," he said slowly. "Some of us will go upstream, as you know, to try and reach Fort Yukon. Others will explore downstream, following the river to its mouth."

"I'm going with you, upstream?" Jonathan asked eagerly.

"I'm sorry, no. There's been a change of plans. Mr. Dyer has requested that you accompany him downstream."

The boy started to protest. Then abruptly he spun on his heel and left the cabin. Watching him, William recalled the time, so long ago, it seemed, when his own heart had been torn because he had been denied a chance to explore with Bob Kennicott.

CHAPTER NINE

A few hours later William, Tonso McCrae, Fred Whymper and Kurilla, the Indian, were on their way upriver. Their awkward-looking oomiak, heavily overloaded with fourteen hundred pounds of supplies, bobbed uneasily in the swift running waters. Tonso shook his head when he looked at the skin boat. "We're asking an awful lot out of that bunch of sticks and sealskins. Might be a lot safer if we built a raft."

There was a last word from Ivan Pavloff who stood upon the high bank and watched them go. "It is too soon," he said. And he repeated the words ominously. "It is too soon." William disagreed. He stood on the bank looking at the ice in the river, moving at greater and greater speed. Starting a thousand miles upstream, it hurled forward with the speed of a train coming downgrade. It came in white boulders, crashing and crumbling all about the frail oomiak. It loomed overhead, and traveled alongside. It ground, block on block, with a hideous gnashing noise like the teeth of a monster grating in anticipation. Quietly he gave the orders to embark.

Only the dexterous maneuvering of Tonso McCrae and Kurilla kept the thin skin covering of the oomiak from being torn repeatedly. Entire sections of riverbank, covered with willows, were undercut and dropped upon the explorers. They fought desperately for survival.

William lunged forward to shove a block of ice away from the boat. "I could explore the river better reading a book," he called over his shoulder to Tonso.

There was no answer.

The river rose in flood as ice jams blocked its seaward passage. Then it subsided, sluggish and uncertain, as it sought for new channels. Huge masses of beautifully clear ice hurtled by, striking each other and cracking into a thousand pieces with the sound of shattering glass. They crouched beneath deep snow, towering like floral pieces on the miniature icebergs. Whole trees, embedded in the ice, tumbled in procession down the river.

"William!"

In answer to the cry, he turned about to see Tonso McCrae in the stern, tense, alert to the jagged ice that moved down upon them.

"Yes, Tonso."

"Another hour of this and we'll all be dead explorers. I advise you to turn back to Nulato. Give the river a chance to get over this madness. It's been saving this ice for six months, and now it's trying to get rid of it all in six hours!"

Reluctantly William agreed. He gave the command, and the oomiak turned back, racing with the current to Nulato on the north bank of the river. Pavloff stood by the water's edge, hand outstretched in greeting. "I welcome you back," he said solemnly. "I welcome you back from the dead. When the ice is gone, I, Pavloff, will accompany you partway upriver."

The boat was hauled high out of the water. For eleven days they waited until the fierceness had gone out of the Yukon. Early in the morning of May twenty-sixth they watched Mr. Dyer and a tight-lipped Jonathan Benson shove downstream. A few hours later, in a downpour of rain, they pushed out into the water again. Ivan Pavloff, in a big canoe loaded with trading goods, preceded them. "You will live to return to my house," he promised.

There was a salute from the rusty old howitzer before the fort, and the journey was underway. Pavloff's trading canoe, with its eight oarsmen, soon pulled away and was lost to sight. William tried to adjust himself to the cramped quarters, but the continual flood of rain wet everything, and made the start of the journey uncomfortable.

Each forward movement against the swift current was a continual fight. The high banks of the river, outlined in dense thickets of willow, seemed to crawl by as the boat fought its way upward.

And there was still a constant stream of ice cakes, logs, and driftwood that called for unending alertness from Tonso Mc-Crae in the stern of the fifteen-foot oomiak. The odd-shaped craft was nearly five feet wide, difficult to control in the swift waters.

The unaccustomed exertions caused the explorers to seek an early camp site. They stretched their rubber blankets in a willow thicket, listened to the patter of rain, and slept soundly.

The next morning they were awake by three, eager to take advantage of every daylight hour. Overhead the ducks and geese were returning in vast flocks from winter feeding grounds in the United States. Cranes floated lazily about, seeking safe landing before coming stiff-legged to earth. Big black bears, awakened from a long winter of sleeping, ambled down to the river.

Occasionally they caught a glimpse of Pavloff and his trading canoe, but mostly they were alone, lost in a new world. Day after day they fought onward, allowing themselves only four or five hours of sleep each night. Once they were seized in a mysterious whirlpool that whipped their battered craft and tossed it a mile downstream before they were aware what was happening. But even in the moments of greatest danger, William never forgot the purpose of his journey. He added a green-winged teal and a hooded grebe to his collection. He lifted his eyes from the dangers of the river and was enthralled by a high sandy bluff full of the nests of the bank swallow.

"Looks like a honeycomb swarming with bees," Tonso observed.

Every third day it was necessary to haul the oomiak out of the river and allow it to dry thoroughly. The sealskins became soft and mushy from long immersion. William seized upon these forced stops to add to his collections. With Tonso McCrae, he broke away from the riverbank, heading overland into the mysterious country.

They stumbled over the spongy moss that formed a treacherous covering for the swampy ground. Hummocks of earth, distorted by the frost of winter and tossed into unwieldy shapes, waited to trip them at every turn. They wore gloves and nets for protection against the mosquitoes that hung like a cloud around them. Still the little insects found openings and kept them in continual torment.

Tonso snorted in disgust as he fell into the swamp. "No wonder Bob Kennicott didn't try to cut overland," he said. "No man in his right senses would stay long away from the river. Wow!" He slapped vigorously at the mosquito that thrust a rapier into him. "Man! Let's get out of here! I'm being eaten alive!"

After each attempt to penetrate inland, William was ready to admit that the only possible route into the interior of Russian America was along the great river arteries. "No man can cross the tundra and live," he said. "If he lost his mosquito netting, he'd die quickly from nervous exhaustion. When the telegraph line comes through," he concluded, "it must follow the rivers."

They went back to the oomiak again, and took up the heartbreaking struggle against the current. Suddenly the sun became a menace. At midday the temperature reached ninety degrees in the shade. They were forced to take shelter between eleven and two each afternoon. They became lost in the aimless channels carved by the restless river, and wasted precious hours solving the gigantic puzzle.

Occasionally they sighted Indian villages on the cliffs above the river. They would hoist the American flag, and beneath it the blue cross and scallop shell of the Scientific Corps flag, and visit with the astonished natives.

After two weeks on the river, Pavloff waved to them in farewell and turned south, his trading accomplished. "I wait for you in Nulato!" he called. Then the river took hold of his large craft and whirled it out of sight around a finger of land.

The explorers were scorched by the sun through the midday, and through every hour of the day and night tormented by the mosquitoes. They journeyed at a time of almost complete daylight, for the earth, in the ceaseless annual cycle it makes about the sun, was tilting toward the glowing ball of fire, bathed in the direct, scorching rays. At the beginning of the journey the sun set at eleven each night, and only forty-five minutes later was rising again. Each day it set and rose farther on the north. Toward the third week in June the huge glowing ball rolled a short distance between east and west on the horizon without ever dipping from sight.

For almost the entire length of their journey the river was

confined between bluffs that sometimes towered high over-head like a canyon gorge. The frozen earth sloughed off con-tinually and fell downward into the river. At times the large bones of animals long dead were thrust outward, suspended in mid-air. William fingered the fossil skull of a musk ox he had discovered on the beach.

"Someday," he said quietly to Tonso McCrae, "I'm going to come back and explore this river basin thoroughly. There's nothing I'll let go unnoticed."

"Someday," Tonso grumbled good-naturedly, "I'm hop-ing we stop long enough for me to get a shot at something bigger'n a duck. This expedition's on the go so much, we're going to starve to death."

"There's your chance," William said quietly. He pointed to a cow moose that had entered the water. Tonso, caught with-out his rifle, bashed his hands together in vexation. Then, without another word, he dove into the river, swam alongside the moose, and killed it with his knife. With great difficulty they hauled the big carcass back to the riverbank, fighting the current that wanted the dead animal for its own victim. That night they feasted.

For twenty-nine days the frail boat fought upward along the river. Tonso McCrae piloted the bobbing craft around the serpentine bends that twisted and turned in vast loops. The mosquitoes never left them, except when the rains came so heavily that the little insects were beaten into submission.

As they crept higher and higher along the swift-flowing river, the trees on either side began to grow smaller and more sparse. But though they were close to the Arctic Circle, the midday heat was still fierce and unrelenting. Checking and rechecking the crude maps Bob Kennicott had prepared from Indian descriptions before his death, William knew they were coming close to the end of their journey, the Hudson Bay Trading Post at Fort Yukon.

They ran the rapids at the rampart, twisted and looped with the river as it reached for the Arctic Circle. The heat was so intense they deferred their start until eight o'clock in the evening. On the twenty-third of June they rounded a bend in the river. "There it is," William said quietly. "Fort Yukon. We've made it." He pointed to the white buildings on the right bank of the river.

Tonso McCrae pointed his rifle into the air, and loud reports echoed and re-echoed. Someone at the Fort raced out, looked in astonishment, and in a moment a rifle shot reverberated in a reply of welcome.

William leaped ashore. He felt like Columbus coming to a new land.

Six days later Captain Ketchum returned from the explorations that had carried him south to Fort Selkirk. Immediately William conferred with him about the feasibility of a telegraph line following the banks of the newly explored Yukon River. They discussed the preparations to be made for the work crews who would follow to erect the poles and stretch the thin copper wires that would eventually link New York City with every major city in Europe.

When all necessary details were determined upon, he decided it was urgent to return quickly to Nulato, to make further preparations for the army of engineers and workmen who would be spearheading the drive to carry the telegraph line across the wilderness of Russian America.

Flushed with triumph, he embarked again with Captain Ketchum, Tonso McCrae, and little Peetka. They retraced their long journey along the Yukon. But where the journey upstream battling the current had taken twenty-nine days, the return was made in four. William, utterly worn, slept a great deal of the time, leaving the guidance of the frail craft to his faithful friend.

At last the cabins of Nulato came in sight high on the banks above the river. The dog Sawashka could be seen, head high, barking furiously. Racing about were her pups, now eight months old, already used to the training harness that would keep them toiling through the winter. Impatient to be home, Peetka leaped overboard and swam to the arms of his father. Tonso McCrae, careful to the end, guided the oomiak to the eager hands that waited.

William stepped out and climbed the steep bank. A stern-faced man, a stranger, was waiting for them. "I'm Warrington from the main office in San Francisco," he said. "You'll want to read this." Abruptly he thrust an open letter in William's hands.

"What is it?" Tonso asked, coming close. William's face whitened. His hands trembled. He sat on a log and ran his fingers through his tangled beard.

"The Atlantic cable is a success," he said dispiritedly. "There's no need for the telegraph line. We're to cease further activity and return to San Francisco."

Then he turned and hid his face. The battle, the toil, the anguish of the winter months, the death of Bob Kennicott, had all been in vain.

Tonso McCrae stood over him. "Don't see why you're so cut up," he said gruffly. "You've got a home to return to. I've got nothing."

CHAPTER TEN

Washington, D. C., July 27, 1866: The steamship GREAT EASTERN *has laid the first permanently successful transatlantic cable. The Western Union Telegraph Company has ordered a halt to the entire work spanning British Columbia, Russian America and Siberia.*

"It happened sixteen days after I left San Francisco last year," William said bitterly. "For thirteen months that news has been following me, never quite reaching me—until now."

"What's our next move?" Tonso asked quietly.

"We're to get the men and as much of the equipment as we can salvage down to Saint Michael's. There'll be a ship waiting to evacuate us."

Tonso looked at him curiously, but said nothing.

It was an odd group that made the journey down to the portage. Most of the men were exultant at the prospect of going home earlier than they had planned. To William, still burdened by the thousands of small details requiring his attention, the journey was like the retreat of a defeated army. And Tonso McCrae said nothing.

At Saint Michael's Island the men were dismayed when they looked out on the Bering Sea and saw nothing but empty space. Young Jonathan Benson walked up to William, shaking his head disconsolately. "Two years since I've seen my folks in San Francisco. Wouldn't you think they'd hurry up that old ship?"

William thought of his own mother, of the year and six months that had gone by since he had last received mail from Boston. Yet he felt no exultation at the thought of going home. He kept looking back to the low hills that barred him from the Yukon Valley and the exploration and scientific work that was denied him. He knew, once gone from Russian America, there was little chance he would ever return.

He tried to lose his depression in work, attending faithfully to the myriad details connected with the end of the great expedition. He was scrupulously honest in his bookkeeping with the Western Union Company, and accounted for every possible piece of equipment entrusted to him. While the impatient men about him complained at the slow passing of the hours, the days for William sped by as he readied the material for loading upon the ship that had not yet arrived.

When he had a day of freedom he crossed to the mainland, hiked along the abrupt, rocky shore line, and explored the teeming swamps to the north of Saint Michael's. At night he and Tonso McCrae walked to the bluff looking over the black sheet of the Bering Sea. Always there would be little groups of workmen clustered about silently, looking to the south and west, hoping for a glimpse of sails against the horizon.

"A pound of tobacco to the first one who sees a sail," William called.

At three o'clock the afternoon of August eighteenth, an old native woman came stumbling down the path from the cliff, chattering with excitement, and pointing out to sea. Far in the distance they saw the white gleam of a sail against the darker sky. While the men ran to sight the vessel, William paid the old woman with the tin of tobacco, then walked slowly to join the group at the northeast bluff.

But he did not want to leave.

Once more he looked to the low hills rising in the distance toward the Yukon country. There was too much work to be done, too many discoveries awaiting, too many scientific marvels to be unearthed for the benefit of the entire world.

During his lonely explorations of the swamps about Saint Michael's, an idea had been trying to force itself into the maze of details that had been overwhelming him.

Hurriedly he composed a letter to Professor Baird, Assistant Secretary of the Smithsonian Institution. He wrote quickly and with unwavering decision. There were two hundred dollars due him in accumulated back wages from the Smithsonian. If the Institution would match the sum, he would devote the entire coming year to scientific exploration of the northland!

Four hundred dollars for an expedition that would span the unknown delta of the Yukon, traverse the sweep of Norton Sound, and plunge into the back country unknown to science. For that sum he would uncover one of the greatest treasures in the distinguished history of the Institution.

He sealed the letter. At nine o'clock that evening, when the first boat came ashore, he handed the missive to a seaman just arriving from the bark, *Clara Bell,* lying a short distance offshore.

"Give this to the Captain," he said. "It's to be mailed in San Francisco."

"Mailed? Aren't you coming with us?" the seaman asked incredulously.

"No. I'm staying."

For five days there was tremendous activity while material

was loaded aboard the *Clara Bell.* William went out to the bark with the last load, and said good-by to everyone. The master of the ship looked at him critically. "You sure you know what you're doing, young man? You know the Western Union Company won't be responsible if you don't come south on my ship?"

"I understand. I'm staying."

He stood on the shore in the early afternoon, and watched the *Clara Bell* get underway. The white sails dropped over the sea. He was alone.

Not entirely.

He turned about and saw Tonso McCrae. The young Captain walked toward him, smiling. "When do we start exploring?"

For the next five months Tonso McCrae was by William's side while he explored the shores of Norton Sound and the wandering reaches of the Unalakleet River. He was with William again on the Yukon while the two battled the currents and the mosquitoes. They plunged into the tundra, and climbed the low hills. They discovered new streams that rushed clear and cold into the gray-brown mud of the spreading river.

Every river that William forded, every sod of tundra that he turned, every remote bay that he dredged brought new lights to dark pages of science.

By the time authorization from the Smithsonian Institution had reached him, he had traveled two thousand miles in an open canoe, fighting upward against the wild rush of the Yukon, then riding gloriously downward on the speeding current. He traveled hundreds of miles on snowshoes in temperatures that plummeted down to forty degrees below zero. Working tirelessly in the long days of summer and through the half-gloom of winter, he collected 4,550 specimens, including a complete set of rock specimens from Fort Yukon all the length of the mighty river for 1,300 miles to the Bering Sea. He discovered deposits of coal, and studied geological formations of rock that uncovered the history of the land for untold ages.

His first love was always for mollusks, but he did not confine his explorations to that one field. In an amazing exhibition of versatility, he made himself an expert in many fields.

The information that he gathered in his tireless journeys with Tonso McCrae was virgin knowledge for the waiting scientific world. The information he gathered on the fishes of Russian America was new, as were his list of mammals, his meteorological observations, his studies on the distribution of plants and animals, and his mapping of the northern limits of tree growth.

Completely separated from the nagging worries that had beset him as scientific director of the Western Union Telegraph Expedition, William was once again utterly engrossed in scientific pursuits. Disregarding the good-natured complaints of Tonso McCrae, he advanced on Russian America armed with spring forceps, a cheesecloth net, and a garden trowel. In the pursuit of hidden insects he used his miniature pick, with one end hatchet-shaped, for prying bark from the willows.

William's complete engrossment was the despair of his friend. "Weren't for me, you'd forget to put your boots on in the morning," Tonso exclaimed.

When game became scarce and fish elusive, they went hungry. At other times they gorged themselves on the salmon from the muddy Yukon and the grayling trout from the clear tributary streams. There were occasions when they shared thick slices of bear meat, moose, and caribou with the Indian families they encountered along the river.

When the nights had grown quiet and cold, and the last honking flight of geese had disappeared to the south, Tonso paddled on the Yukon with powerful strokes, pushing against the ceaseless tug of the river. William crouched in the bow, eyes glued to the two-hundred foot promontory that loomed overhead. Outlined against the leaden sky were the trees that marked the path of the river. From the raw earth of the banks, tiny streams, like wounds in the hide of an animal, broke into the open, and cascaded down to the river below.

"Easy," William cautioned, "there's something in that bank. . . ."

"Easy, my foot," Tonso grunted in reply. "This river doesn't know what easy means. You want to hang around surveying the good earth, grab a paddle and start pushing. This water doesn't want to go anywhere but down!"

Automatically William grasped the paddle, and dug deeply into the water, but never for a moment did he take his eyes away from the riverbank. "Look," he cried, "up there. Tusks! Elephant tusks!"

Protruding from the bank immediately above their heads was a pair of stained, weathered tusks thrust over the river.

"We've got to get ashore. Quickly!" William yelled.

"Doing my best," Tonso said. "Those things you see going round and round are whirlpools, that's all. If we don't get out of here soon, somebody's going to be looking at our front teeth and measuring them for possible piano keys. Look sharp, William. Pull hard to the left!"

They dug deeply, and shot past the sucking pools that appeared in the swirling, muddy river. A toppled tree hung over into the water. Tonso brought the canoe about smartly and threw a line over the gnarled stump. He looked around briefly. "It's safe enough for a while. Let's get back and look at your bone yard."

"No need to go back," William said quietly. "Look there on the cliff." The ground sloughed away with a gentle, sighing noise. A huge section of frozen earth toppled into the river.

"Glory!" Tonso whispered. "It's a dead elephant marching straight out of a graveyard."

William was writing notes with furious haste. The skull and shoulders of an elephant dead thousands of years emerged and hung suspended over the Yukon. Then the river took another gulp of the icy vault enclosing the carcass. The massive body was suspended in mid-air, long, reddish hair plainly visible as the animal long dead emerged above the river. A terrible, sickening odor swept down upon the two watching in the canoe.

They witnessed a sudden movement of the ice wall beneath the monster. It seemed to nod quietly in acquiescence, then it lunged forward, and toppled with a mighty splash into the river. The current took hold of the elephant's corpse, swept it past Tonso and William, and bore it triumphantly down to the sea.

"A million years ago, long before the great ice sheet that covered this part of the world, all this was a jungle, just like Africa," William explained.

"There were cypress and ferns and grasses, enough to feed herds of animals far bigger than the elephants now in Africa and India." He wrinkled his forehead, trying to recall the stories he had heard from Professor Agassiz. "They roamed in herds as large as the caribou herds we saw earlier on the upper Yukon. The biggest kinds of bears were here, even bigger than the one Jonathan Benson shot down on Unimak Island."

Later they camped for the night a few miles downriver. Tonso kept looking over his shoulder. "Gives me the spooks," he said, "thinking of that bone yard, and the old elephant tumbling into the water. Almost as though he were alive."

"He died twenty thousand years ago, at the time the mountains back along the coast in California were being formed." William answered. "Compared with some of the invertebrates I've been finding fossilized along the Yukon, that was almost like yesterday." He was silent for a moment, thinking of the collection he had waiting, ready for shipment to the Smithsonian. "Some of those are a million years old."

"Don't smell like it," Tonso said. "I'll take your shells any time compared with those elephants." He wrinkled his nose. "What happened to these animals? Fall into a glacier?"

William tossed a log on the fire before answering. "Here along the Yukon basin, I've seen absolutely no traces of glacial ice at any time." He paused, looking into the adjoining thicket where a restless ptarmigan was preparing for the night. "No. They must have become mired in the swamps, drowned, then when the climate got colder and all this topsoil became permanently frozen, they were preserved in blocks of ice and frozen mud."

"Blocks of ice," Tonso said. "Reminds me—if we don't head back to camp at Nulato soon, you and I are liable to be walking out of the face of a cliff a million years from now. We're going to wake up some morning and find this river frozen solid."

William shook his head impatiently. "We'll stay out as long as we can. When it gets so cold we're driven to shelter, we'll head for Nulato."

They wrapped in their blankets close to the fire. That night skim ice formed on the surface of the river. A lynx padded across to the island where they were camping, and ripped moose meat hanging from a tree.

In the morning the thin ice was gone, stripped by the swift current. Tonso untied the rawhide thong that tethered the canoe to a tree close to the water's edge. The thong was stiff and unyielding. Back from the river's edge, small pools of water were stilled under ice. "William," Tonso called. But the young scientist stood with his back to the water, his eyes intent on a red fox that slipped through the thin stand of birch on the island. Tonso shrugged his shoulders and shoved the canoe into the water.

The floating ice, in thin sheets one-half inch thick, came down the river in a steady, determined parade. It began to squeeze on either side of the frail canoe. Then suddenly it closed with a rush, grinding and scraping as the ice sheets slid one upon the other. The channel closed, opened again, then sheared inward, carrying the bow of the canoe high.

"We've sprung a leak," William shouted from his position in the bow.

"Shove your coattail in—anything—let's get out of here," Tonso yelled back. "Get back to the shore! We can never walk on that ice. It'll crack right under us! We'll be up to our necks in the Yukon!"

They pushed mightily, forcing their way through the fresh ice. The water swirled in and wet William's boots. They headed for the nearest shore, but an island intervened, and they tumbled headlong off the ice, pulling the canoe high on the beach. Tonso looked over the clogged river, shaking his head. "May as well make ourselves comfortable. It'll be a full week before we can walk over to the far shore and head north to Nulato."

They were held prisoners waiting for an ice bridge to form that would enable them to reach the distant northern shore. Tonso improvised a lean-to of spruce bows which gave them adequate temporary shelter. He shot a goose that had waited too long for the flight south. He stalked ptarmigan and trapped snowshoe rabbits in snares.

William returned from a lengthy walk around the island. He had spent much of the time on his hands and knees up-turning rocks and fallen tree trunks much like a bear in search of succulent insects. He stood above Tonso, shaking his head, marveling at the energy of the young Captain.

"The Smithsonian Institution hired the wrong man," he said. "You're running this show. All I'm doing is tagging along, collecting specimens. Without you, I'd starve or freeze to death within a week."

Tonso blew away the goose feathers that had stuck to the palms of his hands during the cleaning process. "You know, William," he said earnestly. "I love this country. Weren't for missing my folks, I wouldn't ever leave. And I don't think I will. If the Russian American Fur Company agrees, I'm go-ing to get me a little trading post somewhere along the river, and just stay here the rest of my days."

William shook his head in disagreement. "It's not our land. We could never be entirely happy as long as a foreign flag flew over the country."

"Even if the foreign flag meant freedom from hanging?" Tonso demanded. He tore savagely at the stripped carcass of the goose and turned his back on William.

Early in December they were able to cross the ice and follow the trail on the riverbank to their old friends at

Nulato. They received a great round of welcome, then William and Tonso settled back for the bitter winter that was to come. On an average day the temperature was thirty degrees below zero at noon.

With the Indians to guide him, Tonso set his own trap lines up the Nulato River. He was gone for weeks at a time.

William was engrossed with preparation of his specimens for earliest possible shipment back to the Smithsonian Institution.

During Christmas week in 1867, they felt the air of excitement around the village. From the scores of dog team trails that spread fanwise into the wilderness country they heard a never-ending chorus of dogs yelping. Greetings were shouted as the trappers returned to spend the holidays. The pathway leading to the trading post of the Russian American Fur Company was crowded with drivers and barking dogs as bales of furs were unloaded and thrown down on the rough wooden counter. Soft furs of marten, lynx, foxes, and mink were exchanged for provisions, firearms, and ammunition.

Each trapper brought in his family. Everyone from the smallest child to the beaming mother was allowed to choose from the mass of trinkets. These had come from Russia, across the entire width of Siberia to the headquarters of the Russian Fur Company in Sitka, and then been distributed to these obscure trading posts along the great river highway of the interior country.

Tonso fancied himself as a chef. From a variety of sources that astonished William, he secured the ingredients for the making of pies and gingerbread. "Some of the supplies the expedition left on the beach at Unalakleet are finding their way inland," he explained mysteriously.

From the same source came a chunk of frozen reindeer

meat, and a brace of ptarmigan that were dressed to resemble miniature turkeys. Green peas, and other vegetables that had been stored in the frozen subsoil and evidently forgotten when the expedition had gone downriver, were unearthed. Ivan Pavloff and Peetka were invited to Christmas dinner. They blinked in astonishment when they saw the bounteous spread. Tonso and Ivan alternated in singing songs of the South and of old Russia. William, called upon to entertain, dug into his specimen boxes and read slowly from Boston newspapers dated nearly a year before. His audience listened as though he were intoning an original literary production.

Afterwards he and Tonso were alone in their cabin overlooking the frozen river. William was silent, thinking of the long time that had passed since he had spent the holiday season with his mother in Boston. Tonso McCrae, in great spirits after three weeks away on the river, was singing Christmas carols.

"I have my spot for a trading post picked out," he called. "About fifty miles up the Koyukuk River. Greatest fur country I've ever seen. Just loaded with mink, muskrat, beaver, and fox. The Indians are beginning to move into the region. I'll be waiting there for them."

That night William stretched in his bunk, his hands folded behind his head, looking at the white hoarfrost forming between the chinked logs of the cabin, his mind filled with thoughts of other Christmases. He could hear his friend prowling restlessly about the cabin. Finally Tonso came over and tossed a pair of fur gloves on William's bunk. "Merry Christmas, William," he said briefly. "Just wanted you to know that meeting you a year ago was the only thing that saved my life. I was ready to do anything just to outwit the people who were looking for me, trying to hang me. Now," he said, his head thrown back proudly, "I've found something to live for. I've found a country that I can love and that will shelter me for the rest of my life. Thank you."

William held out his hand. Then he said quietly, "Good night, Tonso. Merry Christmas."

William continued his probing into the scientific secrets of the northland. Even bitter sub-zero weather did not deter him from a ceaseless hunt for information. January slipped by without being noticed, so engrossed was he in the countless secrets whispered to him by every tree and shrub that still showed above the snow, by every rock upturned from the firm grip of the thick ice on the river.

On the third of February, 1868, Tonso and William were roused by excited shouts from the natives thronging around the trading post. William drew on his parka and hurried down the narrow pathway. A native whom he recognized as one of the Indians from Fort Yukon was standing before the trading post pulling a worn newspaper from the folds of his parka. He spoke rapidly in his native Athabascan tongue, then, spying William, he held out the paper.

"This comes from the Hudson's Bay Trading Company, this paper," the newcomer said. "From your country. Through Canada, then to the trading posts north to Fort Yukon. I am asked to carry it along the river, to bring the news to all the people.

The paper was dated June 20, 1867, almost eight months past. William shook his head in wonderment as he read:

His Majesty, the Emperor of all the Russias, agrees to cede to the United States . . . all the territory and dominion now possessed on the continent of America. . . .

130]

In Witness whereof, I have hereunto set my hand, and caused the seal of the United States to be affixed.

Done at the city of Washington, this twentieth day of June, in the Year of our Lord one thousand eight hundred and sixty-seven, and of the independence of the United States, the ninety-first.

ANDREW JOHNSON

This land on which William stood now belonged to the United States of America. Tears of joy coursed down his cheek.

Ivan Pavloff came from the post. In his arms was a brilliant red and white American flag with its stars in a field of blue. He handed it without a word to William, then led the way to the flagpole, and hauled down the Russian flag. With trembling fingers William Healey Dall attached the American flag, and then lifted it high to flutter for the first time above the banks of the lower Yukon.

He turned about, and on the outer edge of the crowd he saw Tonso McCrae, grim-faced. When he went back to the cabin, Tonso had disappeared. William found his note on the table.

"I've got to run. I'll be running for the rest of my life. Good-by, dear friend."

CHAPTER ELEVEN

William never realized how much he had grown to love Tonso McCrae until the day in February when he disappeared.

So alarmed did the young scientist become for the safety of his friend that he seized upon the first excuse to search for him. "I may persuade him to ask for amnesty from the President," William thought to himself. "The war has been over for nearly three years. Surely much has been forgiven in that time."

A sudden famine threatened Nulato. The salmon catch of the previous summer had been scanty, and the supplies needed both for humans and dogs were dwindling rapidly. William volunteered to make the long journey to Saint Michael's in order to obtain additional provisions. He spoke to the dogs and urged them forward, and he was alert for some trace of Tonso McCrae.

The wind blew persistently from the north, catching him on the right cheek. He remembered his previous encounter with snow blindness and was careful to keep his eyes shielded at all times. He kept halting, looking for some traces of the missing Tonso. Without McCrae the land became barren, menacing. And, though he fought against it, his zeal for adding to his scientific collection was ebbing. At that moment he would have exchanged the monumental collections of the past eighteen months for the return of his friend.

Facing the wind, his nose and cheeks somehow became frostbitten, and he rubbed them vigorously with snow. He reflected grimly that death by freezing was not entirely painless as so many believed. He felt as though a thousand red-hot needles were being driven into his flesh. Had the freezing continued, he knew, the pain would have disappeared as the flesh beneath the skin froze. On other occasions he had suffered slight cases of frostbite. The skin had peeled off and left a stain quite like sunburn. But beyond that, there had been no harmful aftereffects.

At Saint Michael's he found the Russians still in command as they waited for Americans to come north and claim the new land. The flag of the Czar, before the fort, still fluttered from the pole as though news of the sale had been too long coming, and the land was forever Russian.

And there was no word of Tonso McCrae. William waited four days before starting back to Nulato with the bags of flour. He skirted north along the Sound, looking for the wreck of the *Shannon* and the hut made from her wind-torn cabin, but other storms had come and washed the beach clean.

With a heavy heart, William turned the dogs inland. Yet he was sure that he would see his friend again.

In the early spring of 1868 the Indians along the Yukon were seized with an uneasiness that had been latent for years. The pending change from Russian to American ownership acted upon them adversely. There were murders along the river. Long years of pent-up hatred against the traders of the Russian American Fur Company were vented in bloodshed and violence. Ringleaders went from village to village recounting tales of early cruelties to the natives, urging reprisals before the oppressors were gone from the land forever.

Through all the violence, William Healey Dall, the scientist who was conquering the land for the Smithsonian Institution, moved unharmed. He added daily to the collections that would be returned for classification to the red brick buildings in Washington, D. C.

On May twenty-eighth he stood on the banks of the Yukon and watched the ice breakup for the last time. He knew his work in the interior of Alaska was rapidly coming to an end.

Previously the ice on the Nulato River had gone out, moved sluggishly down to the Yukon, then stuck fast. William was deep in preparation for his final trip to the sea, yet, out of loyalty to the Smithsonian, he was anxious to seize every moment for adding to his collections. He secured a birch canoe, carried it over the ice barriers to one of the smaller streams that had become ice-free, and there paddled along the shore line, his eyes alert for fossils. Suddenly there was a wild crashing sound. The water that had been sluggish and uncertain, began to race violently forward.

"The barrier's broken!" William shouted aloud. He paddled vigorously to escape being crushed between the bluff and the enormous blocks of ice that came racing down the river. He staged a vivid race with the speeding monsters, the little canoe shipping water with every stroke of his paddle. He leaped ashore, dragged the canoe to safety, and fell panting on the hard, frozen ground. Blocks of ice six-feet thick were driven against the bank, cutting off large trees and carrying away vast chunks of the riverbank. Then the pressure forced the ice inland. It tumbled and fell as it was pushed onward by the force of the racing water.

Suddenly the pressure was ended. The water ebbed, and the

ice blocks were stranded high on the land. Thankful for his escape, William nevertheless could not resist examining the ice chunks carefully. There was always the chance that some interesting specimen might be imbedded in the huge frozen masses that had so recently threatened his life!

Back at Nulato the ice was so thick upon the shore that he could scarcely bring the canoe to rest. But little attention had been paid to the rampaging river in his short absence. The Russians were going about hastily, preparing for their own departure. The Indians were milling about, making threatening gestures. It was only the rifles stacked at readiness that kept the Koyukans from assaulting the men whom they accused of abusing them during the long years of Russian ownership.

William found it difficult to get assistance from his former Indian friends. Some were threatening to burn down all the buildings of the fort. Others remained quiet, sitting back, whispering among themselves. There were rumors that all the tribes along the banks of the Yukon would unite and engage in a mighty massacre that would rid the land of white men forever.

William didn't take any unnecessary chances. He kept to himself, busied with the preparations for the trip down to the sea and the ship that would take him back to San Francisco.

Kurilla, his Indian friend of many journeys, came to him furtively, as though afraid to be seen by the others.

"You must go quickly," he said to William. "There are evil ones among the tribesmen who would kill every white man— even you who have been their friend."

William redoubled his efforts. The three Russians who remained at the Fort kept to themselves as though trusting no one—not even William. To all purposes, he was alone, deep in a wilderness country among savages who had killed before and could be aroused to repeat the violence of their acts. Kurilla mounted guard. And by Kurilla's side stood his brother, a native oddly named Monday, who would accompany them on the journey.

To himself William admitted that he was frightened, but he did not dare let his true feelings come to the surface. For more than a year he had lived among these natives without the slightest fear. But Tonso had been his companion for much of that time, and prior to that, the wilderness had been peopled with the members of the Western Union Expedition. He worried, too, for the safety of Tonso in this new unrest that was running rampant among the natives of the Yukon Valley. Even McCrae, strong character that he was, would be unable to cope with the mass hysteria that was rolling down the Yukon like the floodwaters of spring breakup.

In the new urgency that had come upon the scene, William was tempted to leave quickly and abandon the cumbersome boxes of his collections. Then his stubbornness reasserted itself. Even if his life was endangered, he would not leave a single specimen behind. He had braved sickness, loneliness, freezing, and a host of other disasters to gain his collections. He would risk a violent death at the hand of a beserk Indian rather than leave behind one precious shell.

His boxes filled the bidarka. A large amount of equipment that belonged to the Western Union Telegraph Company, material that it had been impossible to ship downriver, he stored in the warehouse, fastening the door with a padlock and chain and securely nailing it. His operations were watched narrowly by the close-pressing Indians. He was quite sure they would break open the storehouse as soon as his canoe had disappeared around the bend.

On June 1, 1868, Ivan Pavloff nailed shut the door of the trading post and walked through a corridor of hostile natives to the loaded bidarkas that floated uneasily on the river. So great was his terror of the natives that he did not turn around to answer William's called farewell. And little Peetka stepped into the overloaden bidarka without a backward look to William. He was crying quietly, and he clutched a rifle to his chest.

"We must go quickly, now," Kurilla whispered. "We are alone."

"Wait," William replied. He shouldered his way through the Indians, walking with firm steps down the path that led by the bank of the river. Once out of sight, he quickened his pace and ran to the monument that had been erected to the memory of Bob Kennicott. He stood by the monument, looking out over the swirling muddy Yukon. He prayed for the strength and the courage that had been Kennicott's.

Then he went back and climbed into the waiting bidarka and gave the word to Kurilla. They pulled out quickly into the swift water. On the beach there was a shout and a general movement back toward the fort. High on the bluff that overlooked the river a thin wisp of smoke curled from the Russian trading post. There was the loud smack of a rifle shot, and the tinkling sound of shattering glass. Then the current seized the frail craft and carried the three in the bidarka around a bend in the river. William wondered if he would ever again see the fort at Nulato that had played such an important part in his scientific life.

And yet there was no time for such thoughts. He still remembered coming unexpectedly upon a group of angry Indians who had pressed upon the Russians. One of them, Tekunka, had spat at the terrified traders. "A word," the Indian had snarled, "and my men wash this floor with your blood. You call us 'dogs of Indians!' We know what you are —murderers, thieves, and outlaws, driven from Russia by your crimes."

Only William's intervention had saved the trembling Russians.

Now he, too, was in danger.

The day of escape was cloudy and cold, with a head wind holding back the natural progress with the swift downflow of the river. Over the little bidarka fluttered the Stars and Stripes and the special flag of the Scientific Corps. If fate ordained that they were to be ambushed and murdered on the trip downstream, William hoped that somehow the flags would fall into the hands of the oncoming Americans, that word of their ending would reach those who waited far away in the States.

He pulled mightily at the stroke oar. The bidarka was crowded and uncomfortable. He saw Kurilla look meaningfully at a hampering box full of bird skins and other natural history specimens. But William shook his head stubbornly. Too much had gone into the contents of the crowding boxes, and he would not abandon them now that freedom was so close.

The river bent and twisted endlessly. At times they saw signs of life behind clumps of scrawny trees. Kurilla bent his head toward the sound. "Whisky," he grunted.

Invariably, when the natives pillaged, their first objective was the stores of whiskies that were in the trading posts. Whisky to them inevitably spelled an act of violence. Drunkenness was a common vice among the natives. They developed an uncontrollable passion for alcohol, which was plentifully supplied to them by whalers and traders in exchange for ivory and furs.

When darkness overtook the three in the bidarka, they pushed close to shore and made camp. Kurilla killed a small beaver. He and Monday ate the flesh of the animal, but William was content to suck on the paws and tail, the only part of the animal that he could eat without revolting. Even in the midst of danger he could not resist the urge to seek among old windfallen logs for bird eggs to add to his collection.

He passed an uneasy night, tossing on a bed of hard-packed sand. In the gray dawn the birch, poplar and willows seemed as gaunt as they had been in the middle of the long winter.

Day after day they fled down the river. Late in the dusk of the sixth day they made camp in a willow thicket. As was his custom, William walked along the riverbank in order to investigate a protruding coal seam he had noticed. He secured a few specimens and headed back to camp. There was a great deal of noise, and he quickened his steps.

Suddenly Kurilla rose from an alder thicket and stopped him. "We have visitors," he said quietly. "A tribe from downriver. We should wait until they are gone."

"No." William brushed away the restraining hand and plunged forward. There were twenty Indians crowded in the camp. They fell back when they saw the white man. Two of them leaped from William's bidarka and scurried away. He ran to the small craft and saw that several of the boxes had been ripped open. A small tin of alcohol that he used for preserving specimens was tilted on one side. But nothing was missing. And when William spun about to protest, the Indians melted away into the adjoining thickets.

William, Kurilla, and Monday ate hurriedly.

"We should go now," Kurilla counseled.

William shook his head stubbornly. "No. We've been paddling all day. We've got to get some rest. We'll take turns standing guard."

He crawled into the small tent, taking the tin of alcohol with him as a precaution. He had not yet fallen asleep when he heard something crash into the tent pins, breaking them. At the same time he heard Kurilla screaming. William seized his revolver, and threw back the flap of the tent. An Indian stood before him. In his hand was a gun, and his finger was on the trigger.

A dark figure hurtled through the air, and Kurilla's arm crashed down on the gun. It fell to the ground and William seized it, and tossed it into the bushes. Then, meaningfully, he lifted his revolver and pointed it at the Indian. "Get out."

Afterwards William turned to Kurilla. "I can't ask you to risk your life for me again. We'll move out."

Wearily they struck camp, climbed into the bidarka, and sought safety on the river.

On the twenty-fifth day they reached the seacoast, and William became the first white man to descend from the Upper Yukon to the sea.

He never lost his awe for the mighty serpent of water that dropped across the entire width of Alaska. In a later report on his journey he said, "We may safely estimate the total length of the Yukon with all its windings at about 2,000 miles, of which three-fourths are navigable for river steamers. In some places on the Lower Yukon one bank is invisible from the other. Above the Ramparts, the river is sometimes twenty miles wide. By its size and the important changes which it is always bringing about in the Bering Sea, it is entitled to rank as one of the largest rivers in the world."

William had no illusions about his explorations. He knew

he had barely lifted a fold of the blanket of mystery that covered the great river. Most of the little tributaries, the lakes, and the pools adjoining were unknown and would remain so for a century to come. With all his knowledge of the Yukon and the aid of his Indian friends, he was still awed by the immensity of the wide sweep of water, like a giant's mark across the broad waist of Alaska. He had great respect for the relentless power of the river as it pushed past innumerable islands, and the channels which it cut and built constantly with each breakup of ice.

He had looked upon the Yukon and seen it quiet, thoughtful, like a softly flowing highway running in peace between mountains and the sea. And he had looked upon the river when mighty whirlpools and rapids had changed it into a relentless, churning demon intent only on death and destruction. He and Tonso had fought the river, and, in turn, the river had aided them, disclosing to their searching eyes, for the first time in the world of science, secrets of botany, zoology, paleontology, anthropology, and archeology.

He was the first American scientist to uncover the virgin territory in the delta of the river. He was the first to recognize it as a bonanza of exploration. It was as though William had opened a new page on a new book, and revealed the land of lakes and mystery, the vast, water-pocked region of the delta, ten thousand square miles of lakes teeming with animal and bird life.

Now the exploration was finished. Monday went ahead to reconnoiter. A short time later he came running back, "Hurry up, Mr. Doctor," he shouted. "Don't stop for a moment! A native tells me there are two American sailing vessels waiting!"

William was overjoyed, yet, at the same moment, he was

seized with a great anxiety. To be so close to escape, and then to miss the vessels. If they sailed without him, it was quite possible that months, perhaps a year, would pass before another American vessel returned to the lonely coast. He left Kurilla behind with the heavily laden bidarka and pushed on rapidly in a smaller, faster canoe.

Early the next day William saw a schooner anchored far out in the bay. He lifted a pair of binoculars and fastened them on the schooner. He could not make out the name of the ship, but pulling away from it was a small bidarka heavily laden with cargo. He studied it closely. There was a white man standing in the stern. Then William's heart sank. The cargo that was almost swamping the bidarka was barrels of rum! The first cargo coming from the States was that which would do the most harm. So bitter was his anger that he resolved not to return on the ship, not even if it meant another year on the solitary Arctic coast.

He paddled wearily to the Redoubt at Saint Michael's. There he learned that another American ship, the *Francis L. Steele*, commanded by Captain Smith, had left a few days previously, but would return early in August. His passage home was assured.

But there was no mail from home. And there was no word of Tonso McCrae.

CHAPTER TWELVE

On August 9, 1868, almost two years since he had leaped ashore at Saint Michael's, William sailed south on the schooner *Francis L. Steele.*

He looked back at the low brown shores almost as though they were the covers of a book that were closing—an unknown, mysterious book. But at the moment he knew more of the secrets of this new America than any other American. He smiled ruefully after he had whispered the boastful words to himself. His knowledge was still meager. At the very moment he was leaving the shores of the great land, he was vowing he would return. He knew he would never be completely happy unless he was able to wander once more over the tundra, to fight the river currents, to climb the low, brush-clad hills.

And there was another reason. Somewhere back of those hills Tonso McCrae was hiding, fearful for his life now that the Stars and Stripes had suddenly unfurled and covered the former Russian America. William wanted to uncover more of the secrets of this new land, now called by its Indian name, Alaska, (the Great Land). He wanted even more to find Tonso who had been missing for six months, and bring him back, if it could be done safely, to his home in the United States.

[143

When the *Francis L. Steele* stopped at Unalaska to replenish its water barrels before starting the long haul south over the waters of the Pacific, he wandered along the beach at Iliulik Harbor, his eyes on the wavering wet line where the surf came and tumbled on the shore. Perhaps Tonso would find a way to disguise his appearance, change his name, and slip south to find safety in some part of the western territories of the United States. It was quite possible for a man to wander across the plains, through the mountain country, and southwest to the desert without disclosing his identity. William decided to look a bit more penetratingly at each new face he encountered, to listen a bit more sharply to every new voice. He was convinced that someday he would meet once again with Tonso McCrae.

Through the long days of August the *Frances L. Steele* crept southward, battling the vicious storms which came to life even in summer on the uneasy Gulf of Alaska. The days and hours stretched out interminably for William. He stood by the wheel as the helmsman conned the ship carefully through the scores of small islands dotting the harbor of Sitka, headquarters of the new American government in Alaska. He went ashore and introduced himself to William S. Dodge, the new mayor, then walked along the dirt streets that still showed the marks of the former Russian masters. The old Greek cathedral with its odd-shaped cross loomed overhead. American soldiers were on the parade ground before the fort, and the American flag fluttered in the damp breeze. The Indians who walked from the camp beyond the town, past the weather-beaten homes in the rain-splattered town, were silent, respectful, awed by the presence of the new soldiers.

William returned to the schooner without having added a single specimen from the beaches of Sitka. He wondered if his departure from Alaska meant an end to his scientific zeal. For he could think of nothing but his return home.

The schooner hurried out to sea again, seeking a wind to hasten it south to San Francisco. The last of Baranof Island faded into the rain clouds of late August. William stood in the plunging bow. Young, eager, and impatient, he tried almost physically to pull the little schooner forward, trying to shove it through the rolling waters. It was over two years since he had left San Francisco, and four years since he had seen his mother in Boston.

Fifty days after the departure from Saint Michael's, the schooner worked laboriously into the yawning mouth of the Golden Gate guarding San Francisco. It eased forward slowly through the brown sentinel hills and came to rest not far from the military post on Alcatraz Island. William was wild with impatience. Once ashore, he walked hurriedly up Market Street until he reached the building that had housed the offices of the Western Union Telegraph Expedition. The building was empty, and he thought sadly of the great contrast between this dark, quiet building and the seething excitement of 1865 and 1866.

Then he continued on for a brief reunion with his friends of the California Academy of Science, the embryonic group of which he had become a member during his stay in San Francisco more than two years before. He was thanked warmly for the scientific papers he had dispatched from Alaska.

"You'll be back," one of the members said earnestly. "You'll be back in Alaska. A man can't become as deeply enmeshed in a new country as you have done and then forget it."

"I hope you're right," William replied. "Nothing would please me more."

He had been traveling continuously for months, and yet a great distance still separated him from home. He inquired hopefully of the new railroad that was being built across the plains westward from Omaha, and eastward from Sacramento in an effort to span the nation for the first time with bonds of steel. But, though great strides had been made, the two sets of rails had not yet been joined. Regretfully, William turned back to the water front, to the offices of the Pacific Mail Steamship Company, and booked passage to New York via the overland crossing at Panama.

When his mother greeted him, she shook her head slowly. "Three years you've taken from your life, son, most of it buried in a wilderness. I hope now you can get busy on some really useful work."

William grinned. His mother would never fully understand his love for scientific research.

He boarded a train for Washington, where he walked the streets with his bag banging against his knees, anxious to get to the Smithsonian. He was dismayed when he saw the immense store of boxes and crates and barrels, most of the specimens he had shipped during the past three years, all stacked and gathering dust, waiting his return. But without protest he pitched in vigorously to the arduous task of preparing the contents for display.

He worked long into the night, sorting, classifying, labeling. The querulous knocks of the watchman each night would bring him to a stop, and he would walk wearily through the dark streets of the sleeping capital. His mind was afire with plans for the work still to be accomplished.

With almost incredible intensity, he managed to begin the

writing of the first of the sixteen hundred short scientific articles he was to publish during his lifetime. He was never without a pencil and notebook at hand, jotting down stray observations or recollections of his Arctic journeys. Perhaps the most amazing part of this year in which he returned from the north was his ability to concentrate on the writing of his book about his sojourn in the north.

The publication of the thick volume entitled *Alaska and Its Resources*, in the spring of 1870, after more than a year of painstaking work with his notebooks, was a great triumph. The book was hailed as an important addition to the scanty knowledge then known about Alaska. It brought together in one volume all the information available about the northern territory, in addition to the hundreds of observations William had written down at every possible moment while journeying along the Yukon.

It served an immediate purpose of bringing to the attention of the scientific world this young adventurer who had already spent more time in probing into the secrets of the northland than any scientist before him. Yet it was not all pleasant. There were some reviewers who leaped upon the book with a great deal of cruelty, dredging for defects, hunting for discrepancies, and making great efforts to depict William as a conceited youngster who had skipped across the face of Alaska while trying to discredit those who had gone before. Fred Whymper, his companion on the Yukon voyage, had published his own book shortly before William. In an ardent effort to show William in a poor light, the reviewers tried to point up differences between the two men, to William's discredit.

Any other embryonic author would have been crushed by the unnecessary violence of the attack. William, the puritanical stubbornness of his mother coming to the fore, sat at his desk and wrote a detailed refutation of the charges. When a magazine reviewer was still hesitant about retracting the charges, William wrote again, demanding that his explanations be published in the same space where the original charges had occurred. The magazine finally complied, retreated in haste, and left William alone to continue toward his goal of becoming one of the most prolific scientific reporters of his time.

In the same year that his book was published, articles that he wrote appeared in the *Procedures of the American Association for the Advancement of Science,* the *Congressional Record,* the *Old and New Magazine,* the *Washington (D.C.) Morning News,* the *Procedures of the Boston Natural History Society,* and the *American Naturalist.* He provided a new map of Alaska which was published by the U.S. Coast Survey, and he even found time to translate a French poem, which, in turn, was published in the *Washington Evening Star* newspaper.

Yet in the midst of all the honors which came to him, he did not forget Tonso McCrae. He journeyed to South Carolina, walking the red clay roads of the back country as he sought out Tonso's former home. There was nothing but disaster and ruin and no word of the former hero of the Confederacy.

Disregarding cautionary words from those about him in the Institution, he walked the blistering hot streets of Washington, ferreting out various Government officials, in an attempt to gain amnesty for Tonso. The officials listened politely, and tried to divert William's attention.

"The man's probably dead. He hasn't been heard of for more than two years, you say. Why stir up these waters? Forget him."

But William refused to be put off. He maintained a stubborn, persistent course that carried him forward from office to office. "Gentlemen," William said, "I lived with McCrae for more than a year. I know him. I know that, if he were allowed to return to the States, to his home in South Carolina, he would be a model citizen, an asset, perhaps one of the leaders in helping to rebuild the South."

"That's what we're afraid of," came the sharp retort, "that he would be a leader. Don't forget, Mr. uh-Dall, that McCrae was a symbol for the South, a dramatic hero who kept on fighting long after all the others had surrendered. He captured the imagination of his people as few others did. Let him get back to South Carolina—and, who knows? A word here, a gesture, and the spark leaps out and sets the South on fire again. We've got troubles enough without inviting some back into the country."

"But sir, you've granted amnesty to all the others——"

"Yes, but the others didn't get involved in a plot to assassinate President Lincoln, either."

"Neither did Tonso; it was his family."

"Family, my foot—a man like McCrae doesn't have to be on the scene to influence people—a thousand miles——"

"It's not fair——"

"I'm busy, sir. You'll have to excuse me."

William met an equally discouraging reception when he sought out various Congressmen. "Let him hang," one of them snorted. "He was a one-man rebellion. McCrae declared war on the United States. You'll never get me to agree to an amnesty."

The previous year, upon the return of William H. Seward from his visit to the northern land whose purchase he had urged, William sought an interview with the retiring Secretary of State. When that was refused, he had sought out members of the Secretary's traveling party.

"Have you heard of Tonso McCrae in your Alaskan journeys?" he asked.

"There was some talk at Unimak, at the whaling station, that the body of a white man answering his description had been washed ashore and buried by the natives. Nothing definite, of course. Probably not a word of truth. And, of course, we had no time to investigate. Quite stormy, you know, coming through the Pass. We felt quite fortunate to be alive ourselves."

Tonso, if he were still alive, had been swallowed by the immensity of the Arctic. And yet William refused to believe that the land could really overcome the fugitive. If any man had ever learned to conquer the northland, it had been Tonso McCrae.

William felt an irresistible urge to return to Alaskan waters. He was not satisfied with the flood of new honors that came to him with the publication of his book. The immense surface of the northland had barely been scratched. There was a lifetime of work for many scientists still waiting.

"The field now open to Americans in Alaska for exploration and discovery," he wrote, "is grand. The Interior everywhere needs exploration, particularly the great plateau north of the Yukon, the valley of the Kuskokwim, and that of the Copper River. The Arctic Ocean, north of Bering Strait, has so far been unduly neglected."

"North to Alaska," he cried. "Open up the land!"

On May 21, 1871, a stranger appeared at the door of William's office high in the tower of the Smithsonian Institution. He picked his way over the jumbled assortment of Alaskan Mollusca not yet fully catalogued, and stood by the

150]

overflowing table that served as a desk for the young scientist.

"Mr. Dall," he said, "my name is Coverly of the Coast Survey. The Superintendent has asked that you drop in and see him at your earliest convenience."

"This afternoon?"

"Fine. We'll be waiting for you."

That afternoon William walked through the doors of the building housing the headquarters of the United States Coast Survey. When he walked out, a few hours later, he had been named Acting Assistant, and was plunged headlong into a new phase of his career—seaman-explorer.

"Mr. Dall," Superintendent Pierce said quietly, "when we published your reconnaissance map of the Yukon River last year, it was the first attempt we'd ever made to put a little light on the interior country. You know Alaska better than any American now living." He spread a map of the Territory before him. "We have acquired an immense Territory, and, to be truthful, we don't know exactly what we've bought. We're turning to you for help. We want you to report to San Francisco, take command of the schooner, *Humboldt*, and spend the next four years making a detailed survey of the Alaska coast line. Will you take the job?"

CHAPTER THIRTEEN

William accepted eagerly. His task of sorting and labeling his collections at the Smithsonian was still far from finished, but he placed it aside regretfully, tried to achieve some semblance of order in the tiny space where he had worked—and was off.

This time his journey to San Francisco was much shorter. The first transcontinental railroad had been completed. William sat on the hard green seats of the day coach on the New York and Erie Railroad, marveling at the speed of the journey. It was hot, dirty, and uncomfortable, with black grit flying in the open window, but to William Healey Dall, the man who had twice made the long, interminable trip south to Nicaragua and Panama, crossing by foot over the Isthmus, then resuming the northward journey by boat again to San Francisco, the time saved made all the inconveniences worthwhile.

There were Pullman cars included in the train west from Chicago, but William, in response to the stern admonition from his mother, had decided to pay the lower fare on the uncomfortable coach. As the days passed slowly by, and the train chugged on from Chicago, through Iowa and Nebraska, he almost relented. But the excitement of seeing the Colorado Territory and the Utah Territory, still a potential source of danger from hostile Indians, subdued his longing for more comfortable quarters. When the train rattled across the deserts of Nevada he became excited thinking of the nearness of California. On the long roll down from the Sierra Nevada Mountains to the sea, he congratulated himself on his thriftiness. "Couldn't have slept tonight anyhow," he thought, as he tried to cushion his stiff neck against the hard green seat.

In San Francisco he went first to a small hotel to bathe and catch up on the sleep he had been missing during the long trip across the continent. Early the next morning he walked down Market Street, his bag banging against his knee, eager to reach the water front and his new command. He caught sight of his reflection in a store window, and stopped short. "Look more like a farmer coming into town than a man going to take command of a ship." He went inside the store and asked permission of the clerk to leave his traveling bag beneath the counter. When this was granted, he continued down the sloping Market Street, head high and shoulders back. He was twenty-six years old, captain of a fine ship, and he was putting out to sea.

He tried to suppress the surge of excitement that swept over him when he looked over to the schooner *Humboldt,* riding the soft swells of San Francisco harbor. He knew others would be watching him, surprised at the youthfulness of the new commander of the Coast Survey vessel.

The *Humboldt* was seventy-six feet long, twenty-one feet in beam. Its five-foot draft made it ideally suited for the work that waited. The crew of eight were already preparing the slim craft for the long voyage north. M. W. Harrington had been named to accompany the reconnaissance voyage as astronomical observer.

One delay after another postponed the sailing of the *Hum-*

boldt. Impatient to be gone, William realized again the terrible frustrations that had beset Bob Kennicott six years before when the Western Union Expedition was inching down the Yukon Valley. Not until the twenty-eighth of August was the vessel ready to sail. By that time the season was so advanced that little could be accomplished.

On September 21, 1871, with William at the helm, the *Humboldt* fought through a storm into the shelter of Captain's Bay on Unalaska Island. White snow clouds swirled around Mt. Makushin, towering a mile into the gray, storm-damaged sky. Birds flew low over the gently curving beach. Beyond, the brown tundra, flecked with the first flurries of snow, rolled like pastureland up the dark sides of the treeless mountain. Another winter was closing in on the northland.

That winter of 1871, stranded in the bleak Aleutian Islands, was the low ebb in William's scientific life. Several times he resolved to resign from the reconnaissance work, to go away from Alaska and never to return. He knew the terrible loneliness of being forsaken and ignored after a brief taste of recognition. He had received no mail, no instructions for months. Once before he had been cut off from the world, but then Tonso McCrae had been at his side, and the days had flown by in a tremendous round of activity. Now he forced himself forward.

He walked the beaches alone in the harsh cold of November when the skies were leaden and the snow and sleet and flying sand were all intermingled in an effort to crush the most hardy spirit. He saw the New Year come in through the gray desolation that is peculiar to the Aleutian Islands most months of the year. He waited impatiently for the coming of the new spring when it would be safe for the little schooner to slip from its anchorage and continue the exploration of the near-shore islands of the Chain.

He never forgot his obligations as commander of the Expeditions. The reports he prepared for submission to the Superintendent of the Coast Survey were detailed, searching, the work of a meticulous scientist. He wrote:

Dear Sir,

The peculiar pinnacle off Cape Kalekhta, which marks the entrance into Captain's Bay, is locally known as Priest Rock, while the inner pinnacle at the south head of Summer Bay is sometimes called the Second Priest. The entire eastern shore of the bay, from Cape Kalekhta nearly to Iliuliuk Village, is more or less studded with sunken rocks, and vessels should give it a fair berth. The first bay south of Cape Kalekhta, is known as Constantine Bay. A vessel called the *Constantine*, belonging to the Russian American Company, attempted to enter it and was wrecked. A reef extends clear across the entrance, and the whole bay is shoal and full of rocks. Just off the entrance we obtained 27 fathoms, smooth, rocky bottom.

A good rule for navigators in this region is to "keep out of the kelp." There is no kelp without rocks, and there are few rocks in less than 8 fathoms which are not marked by kelp."

Then he tossed aside his pen and walked upon the beach, lined with skim ice that had formed during the night. He looked over the low rolling waters far north to the invisible ice line arcing from Siberia to the St. Matthew Islands and eastward into Bristol Bay. Soon, with the coming of spring, the whalers would be pressing the ice line, eager to force a passage into Norton Sound, and the whaling ground beyond. Finally, on the twenty-third of March, 1872, even though the winds were reluctant to let go their grip on the snow-beaten isles, he gave the word to up sail, and the second year of exploration was on.

In the spring and summer of 1872 the *Humboldt* sailed to a score of islands about Unalaska. William took observations at Coal Harbor, explored the rugged and lonely Shumagin Islands, poked into the harbors of Nagai and Little Koniushi and Simeonoff Island. He became immersed in his work, utterly engrossed in a new facet of his scientific life. Almost before it had begun, the season was finished and he was back in San Francisco, deep in the preparation of his reports for the Superintendent.

In 1873, he started his season of reconnaissance in command of a new schooner, the *Yukon*. Greater detail was to be given to the complexities of navigation among the uncounted islands of southeastern Alaska. When he learned of his new assignment, William could not repress his jubilation.

"Buying Alaska was like buying a box of unknown merchandise at an auction," he confided to Harrington, the astronomer. "After six years no one knows exactly what came in our purchase." He pointed to the rough charts of southeastern Alaska. "We can't tell if we own a hundred islands in that area or a thousand. We'll find out." To no one did he tell of his desire to continue his search for his missing friend, Tonso McCrae.

More than 26,000 miles of jagged Alaskan coast line thrust into the Pacific and Arctic Oceans. The swift running channels of the Inside Passage, through the islands leading from the northern boundary of the United States up to Wrangell and Sitka, were studded with hundreds of lethal rocks that were exacting a deadly toll of shipping. Standing on the decks of the small schooner, looking out at the never-ending panorama of green mountains and gray beach that unfolded, William shook his head.

"Four years will just be the beginning of this survey," he said to Harrington. "Fifty years from now men will still be charting these waters."

Armed only with surveying instruments and a theodolite for establishing fixed points ashore, and with a seaman standing in the bow taking soundings of the water depth by hand, William started on one of the most gigantic charting operations in history. The indented coast line of Alaska was far longer than had been envisioned.

In more than a century of Russian occupation the northern land had been off-limits to ships of other nations. True, American vessels had made the journey north during the ill-fated Western Union Telegraph Expedition, but their activities had been severely restricted. Any wide knowledge of the islands and coast line had been denied to American seamen. The efforts of the crew of the *Humboldt,* commanded by William Healey Dall, was the first concerted move to lift the mystery that surrounded Alaska.

Piece by piece, William put together a new map of the northern land. He knew from the first rough attempts at a census in Alaska that 11,000 people were living there at the time, more than ninety per cent of them natives. The few whites were concentrated in two towns, Wrangell and Sitka. By his patient efforts, cartographers were able to begin more accurate maps of the Territory, especially in southeastern Alaska.

This section comprised a strip of mainland approximately thirty miles wide and about three hundred and fifty miles long, the whole known as the "Panhandle." William's first reconnaissance gave definite placement for the few large islands like Admiralty, Prince of Wales, and Baranof. He sketched in innumerable small islands and rocks—almost a thousand in number.

Standing by the wheel of the *Yukon* as it threaded a difficult passage through the close pressing islands, William kept his pencil going vigorously in his notebook. "The partial submergence of this portion of the coast range," he wrote, "accounts for the maze of islands, channels, long inlets and fiords. It is a land of breath taking beauty, a sight that cuts into a man's mind and stays with him forever."

This was William's first view of the twisting waterway that climbs through a thousand islands in the southeastern section of Alaska. It was the first time he had ever looked so closely on the mountains that formed a wall on either side of the channel, mountains that were vividly green, red, gray, yellow, rust, and black when bathed in the infrequent sun.

Almost every day the rains came, a slow persistent drizzle that kept the land continually green. Soft, rolling clouds hung like limp crowns about the mountain tops, sagging downward into the gullies, then rolling forward to engulf the little schooner that labored through the tight passages.

This was an Alaska entirely different from the flat tundra country he had known on his previous voyages, the mosquito plagued deltas of the Yukon River far to the north. He marveled that a land could be so vast, that it could present so many facets for exploration.

With such a small crew on the *Yukon*, and such a tremendous amount of coast line to be mapped, the demands on William's time were endless. Yet, no matter how exhausted he was, it was never possible for him to forget his mission as a scientist.

Early one morning when the *Yukon* was anchored in a

quiet cove on Revillagigedo Island, William roused from the short slumber to which he had accustomed himself. He made an entry in the logbook, and was preparing to recount in detail the operations of the preceding day, when he heard a resounding slap of the waters beyond the bow of the schooner.

William hurried forward. There had been rumors of unrest among the Tlingit Indians. White trappers had disappeared in this area and their bodies had been found months later, showing the marks of torture. Worse yet, bands of lawless men had moved northward into Alaska, anxious to plunder any wealth that might be ripped from the new land. The few troops stationed at Sitka and Wrangell were unable to cope with the lawless ones who had elected to pillage Alaska.

A hundred feet from the *Yukon*, William saw a sudden flash in the air, then the silvery object fell back to the water with a resounding "smack!" and disappeared. He smiled to himself. The salmon were on their annual pilgrimage into the streams to spawn and die. He slipped over the side into the small dory and pulled for the shore.

He was no stranger to the salmon of Alaska. Five years before, on the banks of the Unalakleet River, he had seen the fish in their fruitless struggle. He had kept his dogs alive during the long winters with dried salmon, and he himself had eaten so much of the smoked salmon that he had sickened of it.

Yet he was not prepared for what he saw when he went ashore on Revillagigedo Island. On a half-mile stretch of the black sand beach there were six streams tumbling down from the sea, ice-cold water that had originated in the snow fields on the mountainous island. The streams were so choked with the big humpbacked fish that the water had almost disappeared and only the wet, trembling backs of the fish appeared, packed in solid rows, jammed side by side, moving ahead in unison, falling back, leaping and dying in unison. A startled black bear, spying William, stopped his feasting and ran away to hide in the thickets. Hundreds, thousands of the giant fish were stranded on the banks of the streams, flapping feebly as death overtook them. Overhead screaming ravens circled and swooped downward, plucking the eyes of the hapless fish.

Death was so rampant that it seemed impossible for any to survive. Yet William knew that some would survive, some few would fight their way upstream past death in a thousand forms, and find a spot in the water-washed sand where they would deposit their eggs. In the endless cycle of life and death which was enacted each year in Alaska, the spawning fish died, and floated belly-up down to the sea. Afterwards the eggs hatched, and the tiny minnows under an inch in length swam endlessly about in aimless circles, content to live on microscopic plants that swarm in the Alaskan streams. Those that survived the constant death menacing them headed back downstream as fingerlings and disappeared into the depths of the Pacific Ocean.

For two years they disappeared in the depths, one of the great mysteries of science, for no man has seen a trace of the salmon during the twenty-four months after they disappear from the spawning grounds. Watching the grinding activity of the adult salmon, William thought of the fate awaiting the fingerlings that would survive. Their numbers would be decimated in the depths of the Pacific. They would eat each other, for they were cannibals of the worst kind, and the larger fish would pursue them endlessly. And when they were not pursued by their own kind, seals and sea birds would hunt them relentlessly.

He knew that at the end of the two years, the surviving salmon, then full grown, started beating back through the depths of the ocean toward the identical streams where they had begun life. In spite of the carnage enacted upon them since birth, their numbers still totaled in the millions, and the streams could not support their coming.

The Russians had started a few small salteries in an effort to preserve the salmon and ship it back to St. Petersburg. In his book, William had predicted that the Americans, too, would make some effort to capitalize on this great food potential. Salmon, in time, would come to be the greatest wealth of Alaska, greater by far than the gold that was yet to be taken from the land.

When he could take his attention from the reconnaissance work and his collections, he was dismayed to watch the marauding bands of criminals who had invaded the Territory. Alaska was helpless before the onslaught of ruthless men.

"Why," Harrington protested to William when he came aboard from a visit to the tiny settlement of Wrangell, "no one pays taxes here in the Territory. They've got organized bands of smugglers who slip up from the States. They're selling liquor by the shipload to the natives and stealing their furs!"

Listening to him, William felt a wave of discouragement. All his scientific efforts seemed futile. No one really cared about the northern Territory, no one but thieves and wrongdoers. It would be easy for him to stop his reconnaissance, to turn about, and file an innocuous report. He had a feeling that the material he was sending back was being ignored by the Coast Survey, that even his scientific specimens being dispatched so regularly to the Smithsonian Institution were gathering dust somewhere, unnoticed and unwanted. But the dogged determination that had been characteristic of his young life came to the fore. He would map the Pacific coast line of Alaska even if he were the only one in the entire world who looked at the facts and figures so laboriously acquired.

"Up sail," he ordered grimly. "We're moving on."

The little schooner crept northward through the islands like a white-winged beetle, alone in a green, rain-washed world. Week after week, and month after month, the tiny ship crept up the ladder of latitudes, and inched westward into the sun as it followed the bending curve of Alaska.

Besides charting the jagged coast line, William kept close observation of the rise and fall of the tides at strategic points, noting the characteristics that made navigation in Alaska so hazardous. He measured the silt carried down to the sea by the swift mountain streams. He took observations for latitude and longitude, correcting charts that had been in error for more than a hundred years under the Russian rule. The number of soundings, checking on the depth of harbor waters, was in the thousands.

His greatest achievement, during the four seasons he spent on reconnaissance surveys in Alaska, was the compilation of the statistics which comprised the book, *The Pacific Coast Pilot of Alaska,* a monumental effort upon which all subsequent studies by the Coast Survey in the Alaska area were based. His greatest disappointment was his failure to find any trace of Tonso McCrae.

CHAPTER FOURTEEN

After his third Alaska reconnaissance trip in 1874, William was recalled to Washington, D. C., where he continued to write and enlarge on his northern discoveries.

In 1878 he was delegated by the Coast and Geodetic Survey and the Smithsonian Institution to attend the meeting of the British Association for the Advancement of Science at Dublin, Ireland. Alone in his tower room at the Smithsonian, he danced a jig in elation at his selection. He had always longed to go abroad, not only for the opportunity to visit historical places, but also to meet fellow scientists whose works he read avidly. Travel had been an impossibility. What little money he had saved from his salary went inevitably for the purchase of new additions to his collections. He had resigned himself to a world which was bound by Washington, D. C. on the one side and Alaska on the other.

William left New York early in May and visited the museums and libraries of Norway, Denmark, and Sweden. He lifted his eyes to the mountains of southern Germany, mentally comparing them with the St. Elias range in Alaska. He wandered through Holland and toured England, and finally made the last water jump across the Irish Sea to Dublin where, in August, he addressed the convention on the scientific

[163

knowledge available about America's outpost, the Territory of Alaska.

He had never given up hope that one day he would meet again the man who had exerted such a strong influence in his life—Tonso McCrae. At the very moment he was looking out over the sea of faces before him, interweaving his own experiences in the far north with the scientific discoveries he was recounting, he found himself wondering about Tonso. What if he should be walking the streets of Dublin at this moment?

During the journey he made the acquaintance of most of the leading naturalists of Europe. For many years he maintained a correspondence with the scientists Friele and Sars of Norway, Steenstrup and Bergh of Denmark, von Maltzan and Friedlander of Germany, and leading scientists of the British Museum, Edgar Smith, Hanley, Woodward, Jeffreys, and others. In the period of less than three months during which he met these men, he scoured the Continent, absorbing historic points, museums, libraries, and laboratories of the world's foremost scientific institutions.

The benefits to himself were enormous. Even greater were the future benefits to malacology, the science to which he dedicated himself through his studies of lowly slugs, snails, mussels, clams, oysters, whelks, limpets, and cuttlefish.

Yet, greatly as William admired the European scientists, he did not envy them. He preferred to return to the United States where the fields of endeavor were limitless. He longed again to return to Alaska, which, despite twelve years of his own efforts, was still a treasure house of scientific secrets.

He hurried back to his collections in the Smithsonian, losing himself entirely in his beloved work. The months sped by. Winter became another spring, and rain pelted down on the red bricks of the Smithsonian. He followed a pool of water

164]

that was creeping eerily through the legs of the display cases, and came to a halt before a young woman who held a torn, bedraggled umbrella in her hands.

"Are you interested in the collections?" he asked.

The young lady looked at him blankly. "Collections? No— my umbrella." She shook her head. "I came in out of the rain. If I'm in the way. . . ."

"Of course not."

Shortly before the start of his fourth reconnaissance trip for the Coast Survey in 1880, William married Annette Whitney, the lady with the umbrella. He was thirty-five years old. He took his bride first to Boston where he walked with her by the water front, showing her the wharf of Deshon and Yarrington where, seventeen years before, he had been involved in the attempt to repel the "invasion" of the city by Confederate vessels. In an attempt to kindle her enthusiasm for the little things of the sea that had become the whole of his scientific life, he induced Annette to wade with him through the marshes of Nahant, and along the seashore around Cape Ann, peering into the sea, and scrambling over wet rocks and old logs in a quest for new discoveries.

Annette tried to be brave but inadvertently she shrank when some multilegged insect was dangled before her like a golden locket.

On one point she was firm. She was determined that William's zeal for scientific pursuits was no excuse for interrupting a honeymoon.

"William," she said firmly. "There's no reason why I can't make the trip north to Alaska with you. What other scientists have done or not done is no excuse. Last year," she reminded him, "John Muir was married only three weeks when he left his bride and went away to Alaska for the entire summer.

[165

I'm not going to sit the next six months in Boston waiting for you to return from Alaska. I'm going with you."

As ever, William Healey Dall was practical. Very quietly he agreed. He realized that events might change his wife's mind. He made all the necessary preparations to take Annette on his sixth trip to Alaska.

Everything was serene as they journeyed by train from Boston to Chicago, then sped across the western plains toward San Francisco. The desert sunsets had never been more glorious as the little train chugged noisily across the sand wastes of Utah. He explained to Annette the message of the Sierra Nevada Mountains as the train labored up the abrupt rocky face, seeking for the escape route over the Donner Pass. "Once this was flat land," he said, "and then a tremendous earthquake tilted the entire section seven thousand feet into the air. On one side the Nevada desert looks to the mountains; on the ocean side, the land slopes down to the sea."

In San Francisco, Annette hesitated when she saw the tiny schooner *Yukon*. "I thought it was much larger," she confessed. "It seems so small to take so far out into the ocean."

William reassured her. "There's no finer ship for its size on the Pacific Ocean. Aboard her we're safe."

The *Yukon* headed north with Annette Dall alert and apprehensive despite all of William's reassuring remarks. Several storms were encountered. When the little vessel finally threaded a path among the protecting islands to a safe anchorage before the wooden town of Sitka, Annette was beginning to speak longingly of the drab fascination of Boston and New York. William was perplexed. There was an entire summer of exploration and chart making waiting in a country that would make Sitka appear like a booming metropolis. What

166]

would he do if Annette became terrified of the country at a time when there was no possibility of escape?

His problem was answered that evening.

Even William was shocked at the change in Sitka. The town was falling to ruin. The American troops had been withdrawn as an economy measure three years before. Indians, full of liquor and a determination to right the wrongs of a century of abuse, were marauding the streets. On either side of the path leading to the old Russian castle, wind-beaten homes sagged, half-hidden by tall weeds. Ancient gray fences swayed outward, the pickets wrenched off, splintered, or still resting in the shattered window frames where they had been hurled. Sluggish dogs slept on the wooden sidewalks.

"I've watched the town get worse each trip north," William commented sadly. "This town and Wrangell, although the latter is not quite so bad."

"Why?" Annette demanded. "Why is there so much evil?"

William shook his head. He had been so engrossed in his scientific pursuits that he had paid little attention to the slow degradation that was overtaking Alaska less than fifteen years after the purchase from Russia. "It's the white people who've come north to get rich quickly," he said. "And the government doesn't have the funds to keep soldiers here in order to maintain order." He looked about, worried. "We'll be safer aboard the *Yukon.*"

But Annette, weary of the long nights she had already spent on the small sailing vessel, insisted that they remain ashore during the stay in Sitka.

Late that evening drunken Indians slipped into town. They ransacked the Russian Cathedral, knocked down fences, hurled stones through windows, and raced up and down the muddy street shooting rifles into the air. William was awakened by Annette. "William," she said tearfully, "I want to go home—to Boston."

"But, Annette, not until September will we——"

"The clerk told me there's an American steamer, I think he said the *California*, leaving at midnight. If we hurry I can get aboard."

With Annette gone back to the safety of the States, William was able to concentrate once again on his scientific studies.

During the short stay in Sitka, while the *Yukon* was being prepared for the journey that would carry it north to the Aleutian Islands, William retraced some of the steps he had taken fifteen years before when he had been with Captain Scammon on the schooner *Nightingale*.

He explored the beaches of Chicagof Island, walking in a thin, steady rain that hung like a curtain over the wooded mountain. Relieved because Anne had gone back to safety, happy because he was once again in his beloved Alaska, William listened to the falling rain. It dripped from the green needles of the spruce trees, cut rivers into the faint brown paths of the forest. Heavy footsteps thudded on the carpet of spruce needles. William spun about. The Indians——

But it was a sailor from the *Yukon*. "Everything's ready, sir. We can sail any time you say."

Lawlessness in the Territory had never been worse. The Customs Collector in Sitka spoke bitterly to William. "Seems as though the government has just abandoned this north country. It's pirates who are really in control up here. Biggest one of them all is a fellow named Harrish Manners. Calls himself King of the Smugglers."

"What's he look like?" William demanded.

"I didn't see him. Don't know anyone who ever has. But

they say he's very young—your age, Captain. And he can sail a ship like no one else in these waters."

Listening, William wondered if the man described was the long-missing Tonso McCrae. He hoped their paths would never meet. As commander of a United States vessel, one of the few symbols of law and order in the wild Territory, it would be his duty to arrest Tonso and bring him back to the United States to be hung.

The *Yukon* drew abreast of the herds of fur seals that pointed for the breeding grounds in the Bering Sea.

As they progressed northward, other seals joined the immense migration, all of them pointing with unerring instinct to the tiny, mist-shrouded islands which they called home.

William marveled at the plump little animals, numbering in the hundreds of thousands, that floated so peacefully in the water alongside the *Yukon*, eyeing the schooner with a dog-like curiosity.

"Sail on the portside, sir," one of the seamen called.

William followed the pointing finger. He saw a sailing vessel bear up swiftly in the wind and enter the vast herd of drifting seals. He saw small boats lowered quickly. Men killed the seals with clubs and hauled them into the small boats. The slaughter was sickening.

"Get over there quickly," William ordered. "We've got to stop that murder."

The *Yukon* laid alongside the killer vessel. William cupped his hands and called, "Ahoy, there! What ship is that?"

A bearded man leaned over the rail. He spat into the water before replying. "The *Torrance* out of San Francisco. What can we do for you, mister?"

"I'm Captain William Dall of the United States Coast Survey schooner *Yukon*. I order you to stop this killing of seals on the open seas!"

"Order my foot, Captain. You don't like it, write a letter to Congress. This open sea is international, and ain't nobody in creation going to stop me from killing seals till I can't lift my arm. You hear? Get out of my way. I got some killing to do."

He lifted a rifle calmly and shot three seals in succession, shrugging his shoulders when the small furred bodies sank and disappeared.

William started to leap to the rail, but Harrington held him back. "He's right, Captain. There's nothing you can do about that. Not if he kills every seal in the open waters of the Pacific Ocean."

William turned about and went to his cabin. He was sick.

That night, as the *Yukon* pushed steadily northward, feeling its way closer to the Aleutian Islands, there was a terrible crash, a splintering of wood, and faint cries for help. Harrington came running to William's cabin, pounding on the door. "We've struck one of those seal killers' boats, Captain! Come quickly!"

By the time William reached the deck, all traces of the smaller boat had disappeared. But from the darkness came a cry for help. They turned the wheel and ran down to the man who clung to a drifting spar. He was pulled aboard.

· The survivor brushed off those who would help him. "Where's your Captain?" he demanded.

He stood upright, the water running from his clothing, and looked without flinching at William.

"My name," he said, "is Harrish Manners. I am a citizen of no country. Under international law I demand that I be put ashore at the first inhabited island."

170]

William looked at the survivor steadily. He tried to control the quiver in his voice. "Your name," he said, "is Tonso McCrae. As commander of this vessel, I'm taking you back in irons to Sitka to be tried for treason against the United States." Then he turned and walked away. He could not trust himself to look at Tonso.

CHAPTER FIFTEEN

Not until the *Yukon* had cleared the sheer rock walls guarding the entrance to the harbor at the village on Umaknak Island did the prisoner break his silence. He sent for William and motioned to the irons that bound his hands and feet.

"The seamen tell me you'll be exploring the entire summer down the Aleutian Chain before you turn back to Sitka. Is that so?"

"That is so."

"I don't fancy being tied like a dog for the next four months. Nobody lives out in these islands—except a handful of Aleuts. I got nowhere to go if I escape. Why not give me the liberty of the ship if I give my word of honor not to escape?"

William looked at him levelly. "Whose word—Harrish Manners?"

"No. Captain Tonso McCrae. Confederate Navy of the United States."

Without another word William took the key and unlocked the shackles that bound the prisoner.

Tonso McCrae held out his hand. "Hello, William. Glad to see you."

"Hello, Tonso. Come up on deck. There's an extra bunk in my cabin. You'll stay with me."

The summer that followed was the most exciting and yet the saddest William Healey Dall ever experienced. Every moment of the fleeting daylight hours was spent charting the unknown waters or heading inshore for exploration. Tonso McCrae used all the skill that he had acquired in years of experience to bring the *Yukon* through the perils of the shallow waters surrounding the fog-shrouded islands of the Aleutian Chain.

The two friends explored the seventy-mile length of Umnak Island, climbing the conical, snow-covered volcano, Mt. Vsevidof, rising from the center of the western shore. They roamed the desolate volcanic shores of Chuginadak, Herbert, Carlisle, Kagamil, and Uliaga. Tonso guided the *Yukon* close to Amukta, Chagulak, and Seguam, wary of the sudden storms that came racing down the Bering, black clouds hanging like dirty linen from a dark shelf high in the sky.

He slipped the small ship through narrow passes with a seaman in the bow tossing the line and calling the depth of water available. He led them down the interminable chain of islands with an uncanny skill that was echoed in the safety of the sturdy ship.

Atka, Adak, Kanaga, Amchitka, Kiska, Chugal, Davidof, Attu, Agattu and Semichis, one after the other were visited as the schooner crept ever westward into the setting sun.

The two men discovered fourteen new harbors. On the Islands of the Four Mountains they made extensive studies of native mummies, relics of the days when a thriving native population flourished in the gloom of the Aleutian Islands.

Never during the long, storm-tossed voyage did William

forget he was a scientist. He carried on endless studies in geography, tidal currents, geology, and paleontology.

Tonso McCrae looked at him in wonderment. "If it wasn't for those summers we spent up on the Yukon, I'd say it was impossible for one man to carry on so many endeavors in so many different fields. If they'd just build a brick wall around you, William, you'd qualify for a one-man museum!"

Nothing escaped William's attention, from the mighty humpback whale to the long-flying Arctic tern which swept the length of the world in flight from summer to winter. But his first love, as always, was for the invertebrates.

Scrambling among the rocks by the seashore, he told Tonso of his adventure on Unimak Island years before with Jonathan Benson when the young boy shot the brown bear.

Tonso slipped on seaweed and tumbled into the cold water. "Give me a choice between brown bears and mollusks, and I'll take the bears," he grunted.

"Look into the water," William urged. "It's alive! Crustaceans feeding on diatoms, then others feeding on the crustaceans. There's no end to it!"

"I know," Tonso rejoined. "You told me before. The fish feeding on the little things I can't see, the seals feeding on the fish, the polar bears feeding on the seals, and the Eskimos feeding on the bears. . . ."

"Not down here in the Aleutians," William said seriously. "Not polar bears, not Eskimos. Perhaps farther north——"

"Forget it."

William looked at his friend. "What is it, Tonso? Something wrong?"

The young sea captain looked away, toward the schooner bobbing at rest in the harbor at Kiska. "We've come to the end of the line. Tomorrow we start back." He struck his fist into the palm of his left hand. "No man likes to sail to his own hanging!"

There was no reply that William could make. He followed Tonso down the beach to the waiting boat.

Back on the *Yukon*, William looked to the storm clouds that seemed to hang forever over the mountains back of Kiska harbor. "Set your course for Cape Edgecumbe on Baranof Island," he told the mate. "We make no ports on our way back to Sitka."

On the long voyage back across the rolling North Pacific they sighted land only once, tiny Amatignak Island, landmark for the ships that sailed from America west to Japan and China. Approaching the thousand islands of southeastern Alaska, a wild storm caught them on their last night in the open sea, and the *Yukon* ran like a frightened deer for the shelter of Cross Sound north of Chicagof Island. Then it crept cautiously through Icy Strait, and Chatham, as though grateful for the protection of the intervening islands that warded off the winds racing from the open sea. William ordered the anchor dropped for the night in the shelter of Poison Cove off Peril Strait. In the morning, if the storm abated, they would make the passage down Chatham Strait to Cape Ommaney and up to Sitka.

He stood by the rail with Tonso McCrae, searching desperately for words to say to his friend in this last night they would be together as comrades. "Seventy-three years ago," he said, "more than one hundred and fifty Aleuts died in this Cove."

"Were they hung?" Tonso asked bitterly.

William shook his head. "No. They were poisoned by butter clams they ate at a big feast. We've found out since the clams feed on plankton—you've seen them in this area—

so many they make the water turn a reddish color. Glows at night."

Tonso stared away from the schooner toward the thick forest of spruce and hemlock crowding down to the water's edge.

"That plankton," William finished lamely, "has poison in it just like strychnine. A few milligrams can kill a man."

But Tonso still stared moodily toward the thick forest, a few score yards away from the schooner. Finally he straightened and rubbed his hands together thoughtfully. "You don't have to try to entertain me this last night, William, though I'm grateful for the thought behind it." He looked toward the island, fast fading back into darkness. "I've been watching you through the years, dear friend, even when we have been separated by many miles. I've watched you grow famous. I know that countless honors still wait for you. You have been a wonderful example of how a man can help his country." He turned from William and spoke into the darkness. "I'm never sorry I fought for the Confederacy, but I am sorry I made war against the United States." He spun about impulsively and grasped William's outstretched hand between his own. "If ever I get a chance, if they don't hang me, things will be different. I promise."

Then he walked back to the stern of the ship.

The next morning when the *Yukon* prepared to leave the sheltering cove, Tonso McCrae was missing.

William went ashore at once, searching through the low rain clouds that drifted upon the island. He found Tonso McCrae stretched upon smooth rocks on the beach. By the lifeless body was a small mound of opened clam shells.

William knelt in the sand and wept.

176]

When he returned to the States and turned command of the *Yukon* over to Harrington at the conclusion of his 1880 reconnaissance voyage, William hurried across the country and rejoined Annette. Then they journeyed together to Washington, D. C., where they purchased a home at 1119 Twelfth Street, N. W. This was to be his home, a meeting place for the world's outstanding naturalists for the next forty-seven years. His ceaseless travels in search of more knowledge would take him away almost yearly, but the quiet, cheerful home, under the direction of the lovable Annette Dall, was to be his lodestone for the remainder of his life.

Despite the fact that his income was never very great, William managed to continue gathering collections of mollusks. When scientists throughout the world desired to dispose of collections, William, by dint of much scrimping and saving that reminded him of his mother's efforts to keep the household intact, bought the collections, then patiently persuaded the United States National Museum to take them over at the original purchase price. As a result of his diligent persistence, the Museum acquired an unrivaled collection that has been of great value to American malacologists and paleontologists.

In 1884, William wrote to Harrington, his long-time partner on exploration voyages, telling him that he had decided regretfully to leave the Coast and Geodetic Survey after thirteen years of service. He transferred to the newly formed United States Geological Survey as paleontologist. It was a position he had long desired, for the study of mollusks had always been nearest and dearest to his heart. He was detailed to work at the United States National Museum, and here he labored as Curator of the Division of Mollusks and Tertiary Fossils until his death.

To offset the rejoicing at his new position was the news of

[177

his father's death in distant India. The elder Dall had returned to America on a few visits since that time in 1863 when he had given his son permission to pursue his scientific studies. Regretfully, William wished that his scientific wandering had carried him east to India and reunion with his father rather than north to Alaska and adventure.

A stream of scientific essays and magazine articles poured from William's study on the third floor of the Smithsonian Tower. He was the author of hundreds of documents ranging from articles in the *Overland Monthly*, to a catalogue of shells from Bering Strait and adjacent portions of the Arctic Ocean. The bulk of his prolific writing pertained in some way to the Pacific Northwest and Alaska.

In one year of effort, his name was linked to no less than two hundred and fifty-two scientific papers. Like all his other efforts, he gave himself to the dissemination of knowledge with a burning zeal that allowed him no rest until his thoughts and observations upon a particular subject were placed upon paper, printed, and distributed for others to see.

Not always did he confine himself to matters of scientific interest. After long years of residence in Washington, D. C., when he felt himself well qualified to speak as an outraged taxpayer, he blurted forth his feelings on the garbage collection system of the District of Columbia.

He was alert for any material published about Alaska, and never hesitated to comment in print on any Arctic matters that were before the public. He followed the adventures of other Alaskan explorers who brought their ships to the Arctic Slope, or who retraced Dall's own trails through the Interior of Alaska. Remembering his own life in the northland, he was able to appraise the work of others who penetrated not only into Alaska, but also to Hudson Bay, Greenland, and Siberia.

Primarily, though, William Healey Dall remained a scientist, and his approach to any subject, whether on the early Chinese voyages to America or the study of horseshoe crabs, was always the approach of the scientist. His reputation as the foremost malacologist of his time was secure. The scientific societies of America vied with each other to do him honor.

A fresh generation of scientists grew up about him, young men who glowed with the same enthusiasm that had first sent Dall north to Alaska. When he was forty-three years old, young in years, but already a dean of American scientists, he was able to tell an attentive audience of students, "The only lesson which may be said to be absolutely clear is, that naturalists are born, and not made; that the sacred fire cannot be extinguished by poverty nor lighted from a college taper. That the men whose work is now classical, and whose devotion it is our privilege to honor, owed less to education in any sense than they did to self-denial, steadfastness, energy, a passion for seeking out the truth, and an innate love of nature. These are the qualities which enabled them to gather fruit of the tree of knowledge."

In 1899, he made his final trip to the northland as a member of the Harriman Alaska Expedition, a group of distinguished scientists who traveled leisurely about the Territory. "I'm almost ashamed of the comforts I'm enjoying on the trip," William wrote home to his wife. "It's just as well I didn't start off to Alaska this way, thirty-three years ago—I wouldn't have accomplished anything!" Yet, despite the comforts, the indefatigable Dall completed a volume on mollusks as part of the scientific report of the Harriman expedition.

Years before, William had been one of the founders of the Philosophical Society of Washington. Later he was made a life member of the California Academy of Sciences, and an honorary member of the Alaskan Historical Society at Sitka, Alaska. He was a corresponding member of a score of scientific societies in this country and abroad. In 1888, he received a degree of M.A., *honoris causa,* from Wesleyan University, in Middletown, Connecticut. He was for years an active member of the National Geographic Society, and a member of the Scientific Advisory Committee of that Society. And these were but a part of the seemingly endless list of recognitions that came to him.

Heaped with honors, and acknowledged as one of the great scientists of his time, William retired more and more to his collection of shellfish and his work as Curator of the Division of Mollusks and Tertiary Fossils.

So engrossed was he in his work that he seemed to draw apart from those about him, cloaking his efforts with an extreme austerity that sometimes allowed little patience for the shortcomings of others. He spoke ruefully to his wife Annette. "I heard some of the younger fellows talking behind the showcases today. Said I was the toughest old goat in Washington. I'll have to go easier on them."

From then on he tried consciously to be more considerate of the Museum staff, trying to see in them the eager young adventurer he himself had been so many years before on those first trips north to Alaska. He adopted a fatherly attitude toward the members and was zealous in seeking merited promotions for them. Gradually, with the advance of years, the driving impatience ebbed away from him. The young scientists in the Washington area spoke of "the old goat" as one of the finest, ablest, most considerate and most helpful of the men they knew in scientific endeavors.

From a distance he watched the Territory of Alaska, particularly the new scientific paths that were gradually uncovering the great land, much of it just as unknown as the day William went ashore at Saint Michael's.

In 1915, he was tendered a banquet commemorating the completion of fifty years of service to science. His eyes filled with tears as he listened to the tributes paid to him as America's foremost scientist. Yet when the fine words had ended and his friends had departed, he returned quietly to his work.

· In 1924, when nearly eighty years of age, he was retired from Government service. But the habit of a lifetime was still strong in him, and he continued until his death, in 1927, to go daily to his room in the Smithsonian Institution to work with his famous collections. On warm afternoons in Washington's spring and summer, he walked to his favorite pools along the Potomac. He stretched on the rocks, observing his friends of a lifetime, the humble animals in wondrous combinations of form and color crawling about in the shallow waters. He had an intense sympathy for them, a feeling of friendship, a gratitude for a full life.

The leapfrogging porpoise that escorts ships through Alaska's waters is Dall's porpoise, and the beautiful, white-furred mountain sheep that dares the blizzards of the Talkeetna Mountains in the Interior bears the name of a boy who resolved to forego any position that would not give him time for scientific study.

The name of William Healey Dall is dotted liberally on the maps of the Territory of Alaska. Mount Dall towers into the chill air of the northland. Along with the forty-five mile Dall Island in southeastern Alaska, there is Point Dall, which juts into the restless waters of the Bering Sea. Below it, in the pock-marked delta between the Kuskokwim River and the Yukon is Dall Lake, teeming with muskrat, mink, land otter, and weasel. Dall River comes to life high up in the Arctic Circle and wanders south to the Yukon where a tiny fishing settlement has taken the name of Dall Village.

A hundred thousand spectacular, bizarre figures have tramped across the well-lighted Alaskan stage and disappeared forever. It was left for William Healey Dall, the man who ignored the chase for gold while pursuing a love of nature, to stamp his name for all time upon the fabulous land.

William Healey Dall, first scientist of Alaska.

BIBLIOGRAPHY

Allen, A. A. (Scotty). *Gold, Men and Dogs,* G. P. Putnam's Sons, New York, 1931.

Curwood, James Oliver. *The Alaskan,* Cosmopolitan Book Co., New York, 1923.

Dall, William Healey. *Alaska and Its Resources,* Lee and Shephard, Boston, 1870.

Dufresne, Frank. *Alaska's Animlas and Fishes,* A. S. Barnes and Co., New York, 1946.

Herron, Edward A. *Alaska: Land of Tomorrow,* McGraw-Hill Book Co., New York, 1947.
The Return of the Alaskan, E. P. Dutton and Co., New York, 1955.

Dimond of Alaska: Adventurer in the Far North, Julian Messner, Inc., New York, 1957.

Hubbard, B. R. *Cradle of the Storm,* Dodd, Mead and Co., New York, 1936.
Mush, You Malemutes, America Press, New York, 1932.

London, Jack. *The Call of the Wild,* The Macmillan Co., 1903.

McGurie, James A. *In the Alaska-Yukon Game Land,* Steward & Kidd, Cincinnati, Ohio, 1921.

INDEX

blood starfish, 33
Boston Bay, 14, 32
Boston Harbor, 10, 17, 23
Boston, Massachusetts, 9-10, 12-15, 16-26, 28, 30, 33-34, 36, 70, 90, 106, 119, 129, 145, 165-66
Boston Natural History Society, Procedures of, 148
botany, 36
Brimmer School, 30
Bristol Bay, 76, 155
British Association for the Advancement of Science, 163-64
British Columbia, 11, 36, 46, 70, 107, 118
British Museum, 164
British Navy, 90
Bulkley, Colonel Charles S., 37-38, 58, 68
Bull Run, 17

Calcutta, India, 25
California, 153
California, the, 168
California Academy of Science, 106, 145, 180
Canada, 30, 37, 68, 74, 105
Cape Ann, 10, 165
Cape Edgecombe, 175
Cape Denbigh, 100
Cape Kalekhta, 155
Cape Mohican, 56
Cape Ommaney, 175
Cape Sarichef, 50
Captain's Bay, 154-55
Carlisle, 173
Central Wharf, 14
Chagulak, 173
Chappel, Scott R., 68
Chatham Strait, 175
Chicago Academy of Sciences, 36, 38, 39, 63-64, 106
Chicago, Illinois, 35-36, 39, 40, 106, 152, 166
Chicagof Island, 168, 175

China, 175
chitons, 49
Chugal, 173
Chuginadak, 173
Civil War, 9-25, 32-34, 38, 65-66, 68
clams, 11, 17, 164, 175
Clara Bell, the, 120-21
coal, deposits of, Dall's discovery of, 122
Coal Harbor, 156
Collyer, Reverend, 35
Colorado Territory, 152
Comparative Zoology, 22
Confederates, 9, 12-13, 16, 19-25, 33, 64-67. *See also* Johnny Rebs
Congress, 34, 149
Congressional Record, 148
Constantine Bay, 155
Copper River, 150
Coverly, Mr., 151
crabs, 10, 33, 49, 179
Cross Sound, 175
Crusoe, Robinson, 52, 54
crustaceans, 51, 98, 174
cuttle fish, 17, 164

Dall, Annette Whitney (wife), 165-68, 177, 179, 180
Dall, Mrs. Caroline (mother), 11, 17, 29-31, 34-35, 106, 119, 145-46
Dall, Rev. Charles Henry Appleton, (father), 13, 27-32, 90, 106, 178
Dall Island, 181
Dall Lake, 182
Dall's porpoise, 181
Dall River, 182
Dall Village, 182
Dall, William Healey, works as clerk, 9-12; his early love of science, 10-18; is taken for spy, 15-25; is rescued by Professor Agassiz, 22; is recommended for

Ketchum, Captain, 74-76, 79-84, 85-90, 92, 104-05, 107, 116
Kiska, 173-74
Koryaks, 61-62
Koyukan Indians, 135
Koyukuk River, 129
Kurilla, 92, 104, 110, 135-42
Kuskokwim River, 150, 182
Kwikhpak River, 46-47, 71, 72

Lake Michigan, 36
Lake Ontario, 30
Lake Superior, 39
Lake Takla, 68
Lebarge, Lieutenant Michael, 82-84, 92, 104-05, 107
Lee, General Robert E., 12-13, 65, 97
lichens, Dall's study of, 93
limpets, 17, 49, 164
Lincoln, Abraham, 35, 41-42, 48, 66, 97
Little Koniushi, 156
lobsters, 10

McClellan, General, 35
McCrae, Captain Tonso, 12, 20-21, 32-34, 48, 64-67, 95-103, 110-17, 118-131, 132-33, 142-44, 148-50, 156, 162, 164, 169-71, 172-76
malacology, science of, 164, 177, 179
mammals, Dall's information on, 122
Manners, Harrish, 168-69, 170, 172
Massachusetts, 9, 14, 15, 19, 22, 35
Massachusetts Bay, 10, 21-22
Massachusetts Volunteers, 12
meteorites, 36
meteorological observations, 103, 122
Michigan, 39
Middletown, Connecticut, 180
Minnesota, 39
Missouri, 39

Missouri River, 46
Miss English's Female Seminary, 29
Mississippi Valley, 36
Mollusca, science of, 10, 11, 14, 17, 22, 32-34, 38, 150
mollusks, 14-17, 34, 50, 53, 122, 174, 177, 179
Monday, 136, 139-140
Monterey Bay, 68
moon snail, 50
mosquitoes, 97, 113-14, 121
mosses, Dall's study of, 93, 113
Mount Dall, 181
Mt. Makushin, 154
Mt. Shishaldin, 49, 52
Mt. Vsevidof, 173
Muir, John, 165
musk ox, fossil skull of, 115
mummies, 173
mussels, 11, 164

Nagai, 156
Nahant, Massachusetts, 18, 165
National Geographic Society, 180
naturalists, 22, 71, 107, 164, 165, 177; Dall's advice to students about, 179. *See also* Dall, William Healey
Nebraska, 152
nemertinean, 20
Nevada, 153, 166
New England, 50
New York and Erie Railroad, 152
New York City, 116, 146, 163, 166
New York State, 9
Niagara Falls, 99
Nicaragua, 47, 152
Nightingale, the, 70-71, 72-76, 77, 97
North Pacific Ocean, 43, 45-46, 48, 175
North Pole, 79
Northern Army, 17